TOPOGRAPHY OF TERROR

SITE TOUR
TOPOGRAPHY
OF
TERROR

History of the Site

Published by
Stiftung Topographie des Terrors

Site Tour "Topography of Terror"
History of the Site

Publication to the exhibition
presented as a site information system
with audio guide

Publisher:
Stiftung Topographie des Terrors
represented by
Prof. Dr. Andreas Nachama

Conceptualization, research
and texts:
Dr. Erika Bucholtz

Academic consultant:
Prof. Dr. Peter Steinbach

Editorial consultants:
Klaus Hesse, Andreas Sander,
Ulrich Tempel

English translation:
Dr. Pamela E. Selwyn,
Toby Axelrod (Essay I)

The translation is based in part on
the new versions of the exhibition
and the catalogue "Topography of
Terror," translated in 2008 by Karen
Margolis and Dr. Pamela E. Selwyn.

Exhibition architect:
Heinle, Wischer und Partner, Berlin
Ursula Wilms

Exhibition graphic design and
catalogue:
Braun Engels Gestaltung, Ulm
Gerhard Braun, Eike Beck,
Sabine Lutz

Audio guide production:
Acoustiguide GmbH, Berlin

Printed by:
Mareis Druck GmbH, Weißenhorn

© 2010 Stiftung Topographie
des Terrors and the copyright
holders. All rights reserved.
2nd revised edition 2010

ISBN 978-3-941772-05-2

The Foundation would like to thank all of the individuals,
archives, and collections who placed materials at our
disposal for their kind support.

Special thanks to Prof. Dr. Reinhard Rürup for
developing the original concept for the exhibition in
1998/2002.

Funded by:
Der Beauftragte der Bundesregierung für Kultur
und Medien and Der Regierende Bürgermeister
von Berlin, Senatskanzlei – Kulturelle Angelegenheiten

Cover: Topography of Terror Documentation Center,
June 2010.
Photo: Stefan Müller © Stiftung Topographie des Terrors
Back cover photo: Secret State Police Office,
Prinz-Albrecht-Straße 8, ca. 1933.
© SZ Photo, Munich

CONTENTS

FOREWORD

The "Topography of Terror" opened next to the Martin-Gropius-Bau in 1987 as part of Berlin's 750th anniversary celebrations and the central historical exhibition on the city's history. While putting the traces of the Gestapo, SS, and Reich Security Main Office in context for the first time and documenting them in an exhibition project on the site, the presentation included, as a matter of course, a walking tour with information panels commenting on the history of the terrain. The site tour remained part of the "Topography of Terror" until 1997, when construction began on a new documentation center. Between 1997 and May 2010, when the entire site was reopened, only a few areas were accessible to visitors.

The Topography of Terror Foundation regards the overall site as the "primary object" in the documentation, and, consequently, the site tour as an integral part of its presentation. The few remaining traces of the varying uses of the site in the twentieth century represent the points of departure for the 15 stations of the exhibition as well as an audio guide with further information. In addition, the publication with two essays as well as a variety of eyewitness accounts permits visitors to better understand the broader framework beyond the traces that survive in situ.

The circular tour has been conceived to complement the "Topography of Terror's" permanent indoor exhibition, and aims to introduce visitors to the history of the terrain on the actual site. The stations along the sidewalk of what was once Prinz-Albrecht-Straße (now Niederkirchnerstraße) and the former addresses on Wilhelmstraße provide basic information on the headquarters of Nazi terror and the utilization of the buildings as well as insights into the later history of building on the site. Using further material traces, the tour also addresses the treatment of the terrain in the postwar era – up to the establishment of the "Topography of Terror" as a site of memory. Also integrated into the tour are the two monuments on the historic site: the memorial, protected by a layer of sand, containing the remains of the foundations of the former "house prison" at Gestapo headquarters and the Berlin Wall Monument. Thus at the same time, the site tour also provides a frame narrative: The consequences of what was planned and coordinated on this site – the Nazi crimes of violence committed throughout Europe – are documented in the indoor exhibition.

We would like to thank the architects and designers of the site and the exhibitions, who have realized the Foundation's program and the demands of the site tour with such sensitivity. We owe a great debt of gratitude to the Foundation's former scholarly director Professor Reinhard Rürup for the idea and basic conception of this site tour, but also to all those who have contributed to the project with scholarly guidance, suggestions, and discussions.

We hope that the presentation, which has been extended for the first time to include the historic sidewalk, will meet with the interest of visitors to the site, thus opening up a further dimension in the significance of the "Topography of Terror."

Berlin, April 2010

Professor Andreas Nachama
Executive Director
Stiftung Topographie des Terrors

Aerial view of the Prinz-Albrecht-Straße/Stresemann-straße quarter, ca. 1934. In the center of the picture is the Europahaus complex, and diagonally behind it the Secret State Police Office.

1 TOPOGRAPHY OF TERROR

Between 1933 and 1945, the central institutions of Nazi persecution and terror – the Secret State Police Office, the leadership of the SS and, during the Second World War, the Reich Security Main Office – were located on the site of the present-day Topography of Terror.

After 1945, the buildings, some of them destroyed and some severely damaged, were demolished and the terrain leveled. The history of the place was forgotten.

The Topography of Terror documentation with the excavated remains of the buildings and the exhibition of the same name has existed since West Berlin's 750th anniversary celebrations in 1987. The new documentation center opened in May 2010.

Visitors to the historic site are invited to follow the traces of its past: with an audio guide available at the Documentation Center, you can take a circular route stopping at 15 information panels organized around the remains of the former buildings.

Allied aerial view (section) of Berlin's government quarter
along Wilhelmstraße, after the bombings of April 1944.
Below is the Gestapo and SS site. At center (r.) the
Reich Aviation Ministry. Above (horizontal) the New Reich
Chancellery, (r.) the Reich Ministry of Propaganda.

The Documentation Center designed by the architect
Ursula Wilms (Heinle, Wischer und Partner, Berlin)
and the landscape architect Prof. Heinz W. Hallmann
(Aachen), May 2010.

The Topography of Terror documentation (1989),
two years after its opening in 1987. In the foreground
the exhibition hall.

Aerial view (section) of the nearly cleared site, June 1954.
At center (l.) the remains of the Gestapo headquarters
building (façade and yard with garages).

The border installations at Niederkirchnerstraße, 1990.
On the East Berlin side (l.) the former Prussian Diet
(today Berlin House of Representatives), on the West
Berlin side (r.), the Martin-Gropius-Bau.

2 BERLIN WALL MONUMENT

- ● **Topography of Terror**
- — Course of the Wall
- ○ Border crossings
- ··· Sector borders

The construction of the Berlin Wall began on August 13, 1961. The government of the German Democratic Republic (GDR) built this more than 150-km-long barrier to hermetically seal off East Berlin and the rest of the territory of the GDR. By 1989, at least 136 people had lost their lives at the Wall. Most of them died trying to cross the border to West Berlin.

The Berlin Wall was an international symbol of the Cold War between East and West. The peaceful "fall" of the Wall on November 9, 1989 signaled not just the toppling of the SED (Socialist Unity Party) regime, but also the end of the division of Germany and Europe.

The Wall at Niederkirchnerstraße, which was designated a historic monument in 1990, now belongs to the historical traces of the Topography of Terror Documentation Center. As one of the few remaining pieces of the Wall in the city, it is also one of the central sites in the "Overall Concept for the Berlin Wall" developed by the Berlin Senate.

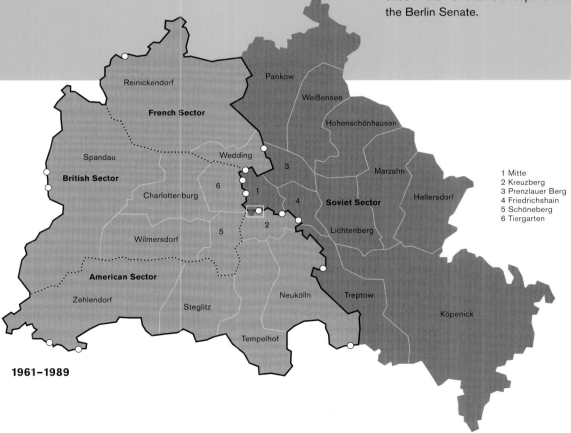

1 Mitte
2 Kreuzberg
3 Prenzlauer Berg
4 Friedrichshain
5 Schöneberg
6 Tiergarten

1961–1989

Military engineers from the East German National People's Army erect tank barriers behind the Berlin Wall at the corner of Wilhelm and Niederkirchner Straße (until 1951, Prinz-Albrecht-Straße), November 1961.

The Berlin Wall at the Niederkirchnerstraße sector border, May 1977. At right, the East German House of the Ministries (formerly the Reich Aviation Ministry, now the Federal Ministry of Finance), at left the present-day Martin-Gropius-Bau.

Illustrated report in the West Berlin
newspaper "BZ" on a Leipzig family's
escape to West Berlin using a
homemade ropeway from the roof
of the East German House of the
Ministries, July 30, 1965.

Von diesem Dach...
"rollte" Familie Holz-
apfel in die Freiheit. (Ge-
strichelte Linie.)

Nach der Flucht...
kletterte ein Grepo-Offizier
auf die Mauer, um das ge-
kappte Stahlseil einzurollen.

DAS IST DIE "SCHLEICHSOCKE". Jedes Familienmitglied trug sie,
um auch das geringste Geräusch zu vermeiden.

KAUM AUF WESTBERLINER GEBIET, wurde der neunjährige
Günter von seinen Eltern ins Bett gebracht.

Spectators after the "fall" of the Berlin Wall,
at Niederkirchner and Wilhelm Straße,
November 12, 1989.

Secret State Police Office, Prinz-Albrecht-Straße 8, ca. 1936.

3 PRINZ-ALBRECHT-STRASSE 8 GESTAPO HEADQUARTERS

The building at Prinz-Albrecht-Straße 8 was built between 1901 and 1905 as a school of industrial arts and crafts. From 1933 to 1945, it was the headquarters of the Secret State Police Office, which together with the SS became the Nazi regime's central instrument of power and terror throughout the German territories. It housed the offices of Heinrich Himmler, the Reich SS Leader and Chief of the German Police, Reinhard Heydrich, the Chief of the Security Police and the SD, and many of the other individuals who were chiefly responsible for the mass crimes of the Nazis. In the south wing, the Gestapo set up a "house prison" in 1933. From 1939 on the building was also the headquarters of the Reich Security Main Office.

Gestapo headquarters was bombed several times by the Allies during the Second World War. The building, which, although burnt-out, was considered capable of reconstruction, was partially demolished in 1953–54. The remainder was blown up in 1956.

Today one can still see the segmental arch of the main portal, remains of the cellar walls, and portions of the former sidewalk.

Prussian Minister President Hermann Göring bestows the
leadership of the Prussian Gestapo on Heinrich Himmler
(r., in SS uniform), in the lecture hall of the old School of
Industrial Arts and Crafts, April 20, 1934.

Internal meeting at the Secret State Police Office, ca. 1936.
Heinrich Himmler, Reich SS Leader and Chief of the German Police (2nd fr. r.), Reinhard Heydrich, Chief of the Security Police and the SD (2nd fr. l.), Karl Wolff, Chief of the Reich SS Leader's Personal Staff (r.), and Werner Lorenz, later head of the Ethnic German Liaison Office.

Staircase in the central tract of the building at Prinz-Albrecht-Straße 8, ca. 1936.

The façade of the former Gestapo headquarters is blown up, June 1956.

Secret State Police Office, Prinz-Albrecht-Straße 8.
In the foreground at left is the perimeter wall with the
entrance to the courtyard, ca. 1933.

4 PRINZ-ALBRECHT-STRASSE 8 MAIN DRIVEWAY TO GESTAPO HEADQUARTERS

In 1936 the Gestapo had a block of garages built next to the main building of the Secret State Police Office. Plans for an additional office building, however, were postponed. In 1937 there were again plans to erect a new building on the street side. This building, conceived as a "preliminary extension of the Secret State Police Office," was also never realized.

The driveway on Prinz-Albrecht-Straße led not only to the block of garages. Transports of prisoners to the Gestapo "house prison" in the south wing of the main building also had to take this "east gate."

After the ruins of Gestapo headquarters were blown up in 1956, the remains of the garage installation were also removed.

The cobblestone pavement and lowered curbstone of the former entrance are still preserved. The piers of the "east gate" that survived the clearance of rubble on the site now lie in the exhibition trench.

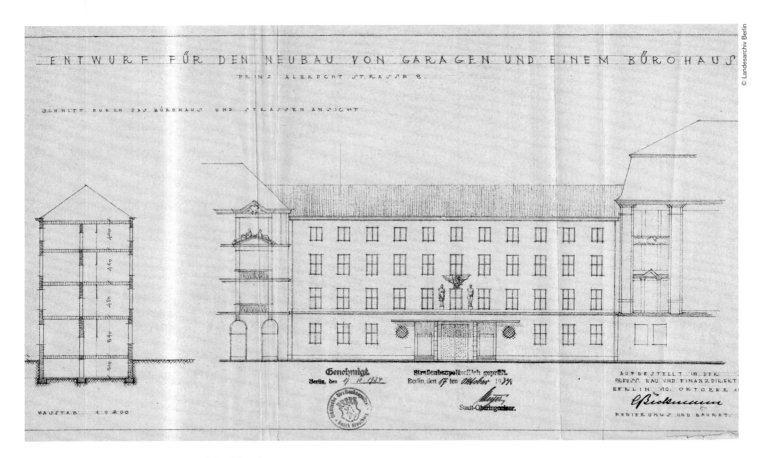

ENTWURF FÜR DEN NEUBAU VON GARAGEN UND EINEM BÜROHAUS

PRINZ ALBRECHT STRASSE 8.

SCHNITT DURCH DAS BÜROHAUS UND STRASSEN ANSICHT

Plans for a new Gestapo office building, Prinz-Albrecht-Straße 8 (street view), prepared by the Prussian Department of Building and Finance, October 1934.

Prisoner transport van and SS guards in the yard of Columbia concentration camp, Berlin-Tempelhof, 1935–36.

The former Gestapo headquarters at Prinz-Albrecht-Straße 8 (aerial view), 1945–46 (annotations on photo from 1992).

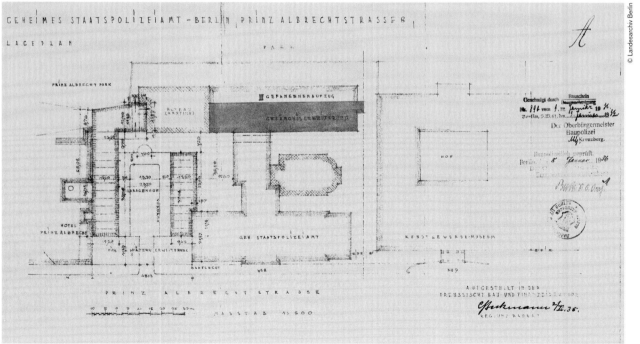

Site plan of the Secret State Police Office with the courtyard garages, the prison extension, and the reference to a new office building ("for future expansion"), prepared by the Prussian Department of Building and Finance, January 1936.

Hotel Prinz Albrecht, Prinz-Albrecht-Straße 9,
1932–33.

5 PRINZ-ALBRECHT-STRASSE 9
HOTEL PRINZ ALBRECHT

The Hotel Prinz Albrecht, originally built in 1887–88 as the Hotel Römerbad, was still considered a first-rate hotel in the Weimar Republic. It was a meeting place for the National Socialist German Workers' Party (NSDAP) even before 1933.

In the autumn of 1934, the hotel was turned into the SS House when Reich SS Leader Heinrich Himmler moved the most important offices of the SS leadership from Munich to Berlin. These included the Adjutancy (later Main Office of the Reich SS Leader's Personal Staff), the administrative headquarters (later SS Main Office) and the later Personnel Chancellery. During the war, Himmler had plans to expand the Personal Staff's central building over the Prinz-Albrecht-Straße/Saarlandstraße quarter, but they were never realized.

In 1943, the SS House was almost completely destroyed by a high explosive bomb.

Two cobblestone driveways on the eastern side of the building and remains of the cellar walls are still visible today.

Adolf Hitler and Joseph Goebbels (3rd fr. r.) leaving the Hotel Prinz Albrecht after the constitutive meeting of the Nazi Party parliamentary faction in the Prussian Diet, May 19, 1932.

In German-occupied Ukraine, autumn 1942. Heinrich Himmler, Reich SS Leader and Chief of the German Police (2nd fr. r.), Hans Adolf Prützmann, Superior SS and Police Leader for southern Russia and the Ukraine (2nd fr. l.), Karl Wolff, Chief of the Main Office of the Reich SS Leader's Personal Staff (3rd fr. r.), and Werner Grothmann, Himmler's adjutant (l.).

The junction of Wilhelm and Prinz-Albrecht-Straße, 1944–45. At center, the bombed-out corner building at Wilhelmstraße 98, next to it the rubble of the SS House with Gestapo headquarters in the background.

Allied aerial view (section) of the Prinz-Albrecht, Wilhelm and Saarland Straße quarter. In the center are the gardens of Prinz Albrecht Palais, at left the Europahaus complex, September 1943.

Wilhelmstraße during the funeral ceremonies for the
chief of the Reich Security Main Office Reinhard Heydrich,
June 8, 1942. At left the Prinz Albrecht Palais.

6 WILHELMSTRASSE 98–101 GESTAPO AND SS OFFICES

From the mid-1930s on, the majority of residential and commercial buildings on Wilhelmstraße (98–107) housed offices of the Secret State Police and SS. Several of the buildings underwent remodeling or such measures were planned. For several months in early 1936, Wilhelmstraße 98 also served as headquarters for the Inspectorate of Concentration Camps.

In 1936–37 there were plans to replace the buildings at Wilhelmstraße 98–101 and the neighboring former Hotel Prinz Albrecht with a monumental new building for the Gestapo, but they were never realized. Instead, the offices of the Gestapo and SS gradually spread throughout the city.

The buildings at Wilhelmstraße 98–101 were largely destroyed during the Second World War. The site had been cleared by the early 1960s.

Portions of the buildings' outer walls remain.

Residential and commercial building
at Wilhelmstraße 100, undated.

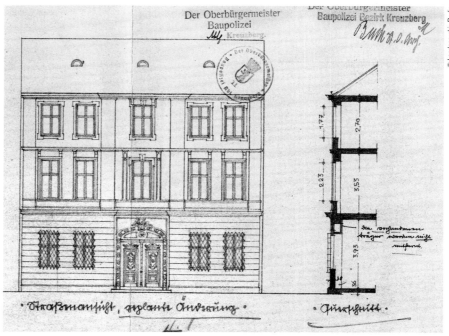

Plan for the remodeling of the building at
Wilhelmstraße 100, street view, December 1935.

Ruins of the buildings at Wilhelmstraße 98–101.
At the edge of the photo (r.) is the former Reich Aviation
Ministry, 1948.

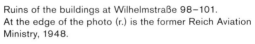

Visit to Dachau concentration camp, May 8, 1936.
Heinrich Himmler, Reich SS Leader, Rudolf Heß, the
Führer's Deputy (r.), and Karl Wolff, Himmler's chief
adjutant, in front of a signpost erected near the camp.

Colonnade and façades of the Prinz Albrecht Palais
on Wilhelmstraße, 1941–42.

7 WILHELMSTRASSE 102
PRINZ ALBRECHT PALAIS

The Prinz Albrecht Palais, built in 1737–39 as the baroque Palais Vernezobre, was remodeled by Karl Friedrich Schinkel for Prince Albrecht of Prussia in 1830–32. During the Weimar Republic, the former royal family, the Hohenzollern, rented the palace out as a guesthouse for official visitors on several occasions.

At the end of 1934, the Security Service (SD) of the SS moved into the Palais. In 1939 it became part of the newly established Reich Security Main Office, which as the headquarters of Nazi terror throughout Europe was responsible for the murder of millions during the Second World War. In 1941, work began on expanding the imposing Palais to serve as the official head-quarters of the chief of the Reich Security Main Office Reinhard Heydrich, who was succeeded by Ernst Kaltenbrunner in 1943.

The Palais interior was severely damaged by bombing in November 1943. The ruins, which could have been reconstructed, were blown up in 1949.

What remain today are the foundation wall of the colonnade and the former driveways to the Palais.

Main façade of the Prinz Albrecht Palais facing the forecourt on Wilhelmstraße, ca. 1930.

Forecourt of the Prinz Albrecht Palais. During the funeral ceremonies for Reinhard Heydrich, the most important department heads and staff members of the Reich Security Main Office escort the coffin from Heydrich's headquarters to the New Reich Chancellery, June 9, 1942. Front row, fr. l.: Arthur Nebe, head of Department V (Criminal Investigation Police), Bruno Streckenbach, head of Department I (Personnel), and Heinrich Müller, head of Department IV (Gestapo).

The bombed-out Prinz Albrecht Palais seen through
the ruined colonnade on Wilhelmstraße, 1947.

Office of the chief of the Reich Security Main Office
after the restoration of the Palais, ca. 1942.

Annex to the Prinz Albrecht Palais,
Wilhelmstraße 103–104, undated.

8 WILHELMSTRASSE 103–104 OFFICE BUILDING OF THE SD

Wilhelmstraße 103–104 was an annex to the Prinz Albrecht Palais. The SS rented it from the Hohenzollern in 1934 at about the same time as they moved into the Palais. A few months later, the remodeling of the front and rear buildings was completed, along with numerous new offices and a dormitory wing for the Security Service of the SS (SS Security Main Office), which was active as the Nazi Party's domestic and foreign intelligence service.

The Security Service (SD) of the SS used the part of the Prinz Albrecht gardens adjacent to the courtyards at Wilhelmstraße 105–106 for its growing fleet of vehicles. In 1937, a construction permit was issued to build a one-storey garage here.

The building at Wilhelmstraße 103–104 was severely damaged during the Second World War. The ruins were blown up in 1953.

What remains today is the cobblestone driveway that led through the building to the courtyard.

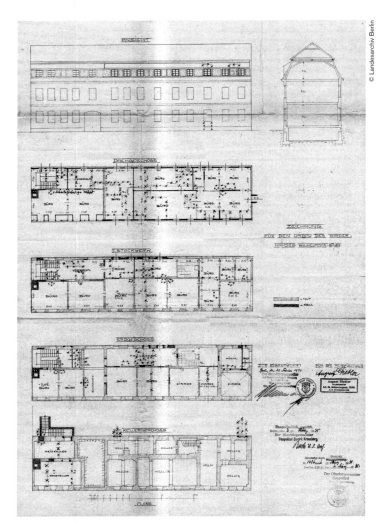

Plans for the remodeling of the front building at
Wilhelmstraße 103–104 with an expansion of the attic
for the offices of the Security Service of the SS,
February–March 1935.

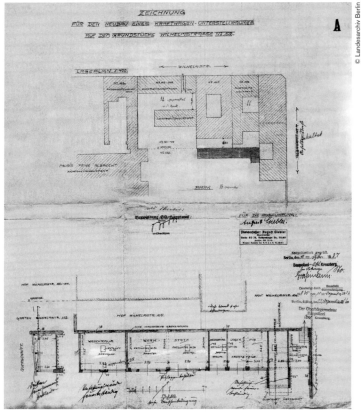

Drawing "for the construction of a new garage" at the plot
boundary of Wilhelmstraße 105–106, December 1937.

The rubble of the Prinz Albrecht Palais (center) and the cleared plot Wilhelmstraße 103–104, 1956.

Der Chef der Sicherheitspolizei
und des SD
Amt III

Berlin SW 11, den 12. Mai 1941
Prinz-Albrecht-Straße 8
für Rückfragen 12 00 30/244

Geheim! 247

Persönlich sofort vorlegen!

Meldungen
aus dem Reich

Nr. 185

Vorliegender Bericht ist nur persönlich
für den Adressaten bestimmt und enthält
Nachrichtenmaterial, das der Aktualität
wegen **unüberprüft** übersandt wird.

Cover of the SD's "Reports from the Reich,"
no. 185, May 12, 1941.

Building housing the publishing and editorial offices
of "Der Angriff," Wilhelmstraße 106, 1933.

9 WILHELMSTRASSE 106 THE "ANGRIFF" BUILDING

From 1932 on, the commercial building at Wilhelmstraße 106 erected in 1903 housed the editorial offices of the Nazi newspaper "Der Angriff" (The Attack), founded by Joseph Goebbels. Various plans for remodeling or expansion existed for the building acquired by the publishing company of the same name.

In July 1934, the adjutancy of the newly appointed SA chief of staff Viktor Lutze – successor to the murdered Ernst Röhm – moved into the building, which from 1935 also served as the office of the SA's Berlin-Brandenburg group leadership.

From 1937 to 1945, various departments of the Security Service (SD) of the SS used the building. During this period, the basement was converted into a subterranean garage for the SD's fleet of vehicles and equipped with air raid shelters.

A 1945 map of war damage to Berlin lists the building under the rubric "partial damage." It was nevertheless demolished along with the rest of the ruins.

Today a cobblestone driveway and fragments of the outer walls survive.

Front page of the Nazi evening paper "Der Angriff" (The Attack) with an article on Röhm's arrest, June 30, 1934.

der Angriff

Die nationalsozialistische Abendzeitung

8. Jahrgang Nr. 151 — 30. Juni 1934 Sonnabend

Hitler reißt den Meuterern die Achselstücke von der Schulter

Mit eiserner Entschlossenheit das Treiben der Verschwörer beendet

Der Luxus wird ausgerottet
Höheres Strafmaß für SA-Führer als für Nicht-Nationalsozialisten

Der Auftrag des neuen Stabschefs

Der Führer spricht zu den SA-Führern

Site plan of the building of "Der Angriff" and the neighboring hotel, June 1933. At left: plans to break through the firewall in order to link the two buildings.

SA Chief of Staff Viktor Lutze (successor to Ernst Röhm)
leaving Wilhelmstraße 106, July 24, 1934.

The corner of Wilhelm and Anhalter Straße with the ruins
of the building at Wilhelmstraße 106, 1948.

Hitler's motorcade on its way from the Reich Chancellery
to Anhalter Bahnhof on the occasion of his departure
for an official visit to Italy, corner of Wilhelm and Anhalter
Straße, May 2, 1938.

10 ANHALTER STRASSE 13
(WILHELMSTRASSE 107)
HOTEL WARTBURG

Apart from Wilhelmstraße 105, the Hotel Wartburg was the only building near the Prinz Albrecht Palais not to house offices of the Secret State Police or SS. For a time, however, there had also been plans for the Gestapo to use the hotel.

The most extensive plans for new construction on the site existed in 1937 in the form of two large buildings for the Gestapo and SS. Had they been realized, all of the structures on Wilhelmstraße (98–107) – with the exception of the Prinz Albrecht Palais – would have had to be demolished, along with the former Hotel Prinz Albrecht. In addition, from 1937 there were also plans for new office buildings on the North-South Axis developed by Albert Speer, General Building Inspector for the Reich Capital Berlin, as part of the planning for the city of "Germania."

The Hotel Wartburg was badly destroyed in the Second World War.

Fragments of the foundations have been preserved.

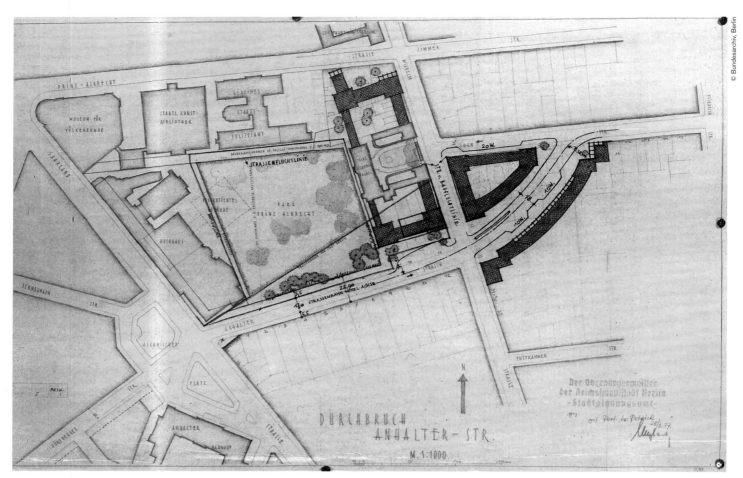

Plans for two new office buildings for the Secret State Police (North Building) and the Security Service of the SS (South Building) next to the Prinz Albrecht Palais, June 1937.

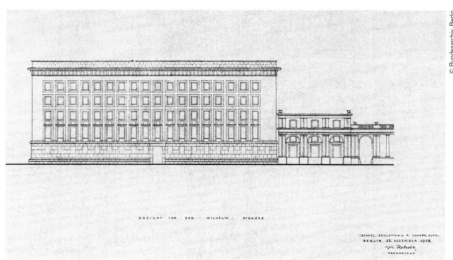

Preliminary sketch by the Department of Public Works for an office building for the Security Service of the SS, view from Wilhelmstraße, December 1938. The main entrance to the building was planned for Anhalter Straße.

Model of the North-South Axis planned by Albert Speer for the future capital "Germania." Central segment between South Station (below) and the Great Hall (above), planning as of March 1940. The upper portion of the photo (r.) shows the site of the Reich Security Main Office.

The cleared site at Wilhelmstraße, 1959.
In the background (l.) are the ruins of Anhalter Bahnhof.

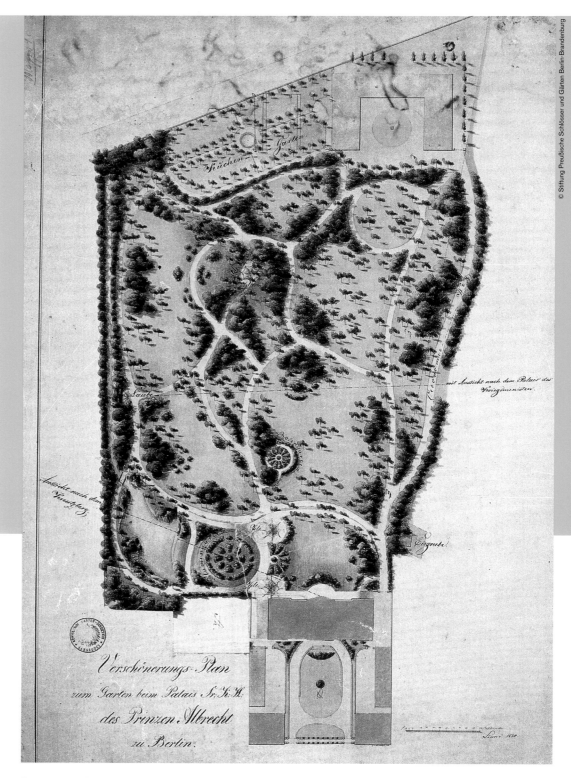

"Improvement Plan" for the gardens of Prinz Albrecht
Palais by Peter Joseph Lenné, 1830.

11 THE GARDENS OF PRINZ ALBRECHT PALAIS

The baroque Palais Vernezobre included formal gardens in the French manner. In 1830, when the palace was remodeled by Karl Friedrich Schinkel, Peter Joseph Lenné laid out landscape gardens in the English style.

In the 1920s, the Europahaus complex was built on the western part of the gardens. During the Nazi period, temporary buildings and an air raid shelter were constructed on the edge of the gardens. Air raid protection ditches and a static fire tank were also added.

The clearing of rubble from the area after the war left a leveled open space in the early 1960s. Several land use plans were developed in the years that followed, but none were realized.

The remains of the concrete and asphalt tracks through the grove of locust trees that grew spontaneously are from the 1970s and 1980s, when there was an "Autodrom" here where people could drive without a license.

US Air Force reconnaissance photo (section) after
the bombing on February 3, 1945. The lower middle
part of the photo shows the heavily damaged site
of the Reich Security Main Office.

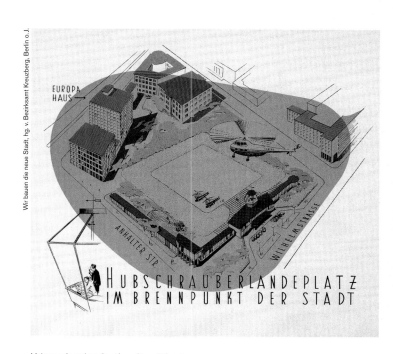

Urban planning for the site of the former
Prinz Albrecht Palais, 1956.

A construction recycling firm uses the former
Gestapo site, view from the Martin-Gropius-Bau
towards Wilhelmstraße, 1981.

The "Autodrom" on the site of the former
Prinz Albrecht gardens, 1981.

The Europahaus complex at Askanischer Platz
with the unfinished mounts for neon signs, 1931.

12 SAARLANDSTRASSE 90–102 EUROPAHAUS COMPLEX

The gardens of Prinz Albrecht Palais originally extended to König-grätzer Straße (now Stresemannstraße). During the Weimar Republic, the Hohenzollern sold the portion of the gardens along the street, on which the Europahaus complex was built in the years 1926–31. Further plans to construct a high-rise hotel on the rest of the garden site were not realized.

The Europahaus complex was run largely as a cultural and leisure center, whose outdoor dance floor was immediately adjacent to Gestapo headquarters after 1933. In 1941, Reich SS Leader Heinrich Himmler also considered using the Europahaus, which was occupied by the Reich Ministry of Labor, as a central office building for the Personal Staff.

The building complex was severely damaged during the Second World War, but largely restored after 1945.

Today the Europahaus houses the Federal Ministry of Economic Cooperation and Development.

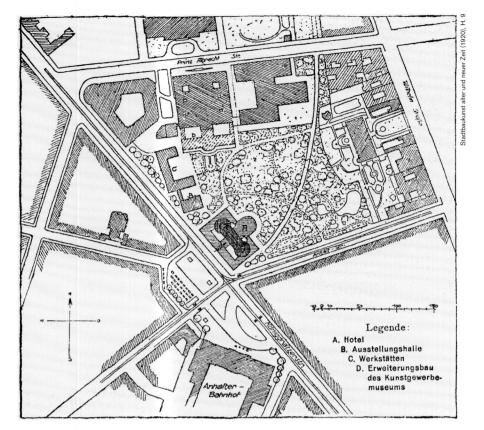

Legende:
A. Hotel
B. Ausstellungshalle
C. Werkstätten
D. Erweiterungsbau
   des Kunstgewerbe-
   museums

Bruno Möhring's plans for the redesigning
and use of the Prinz Albrecht gardens,
site plan, 1920.

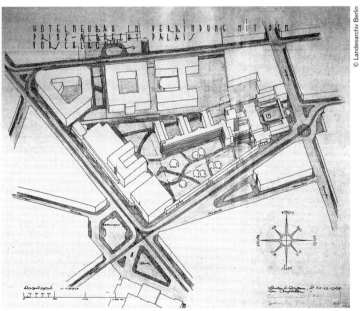

Design by Jürgen Bachmann and Julius Hey for a
new hotel "in conjunction with the Prinz Albrecht Palais,"
site plan, 1928.

The Europahaus complex's outdoor dance floor in the
summer, ca. 1933.

The burnt-out Europahaus complex on Saarlandstraße
(renamed Stresemannstraße in 1947), 1945.

The Reich Security Main Office air raid bunker,
built in 1941, after the Second World War, 1951.

13 NAZI AIR RAID PROTECTION STRUCTURES

The Nazis already began constructing air raid protection for Berlin in 1933. In the buildings on Prinz Albrecht and Wilhelm Straße used by the Gestapo and SS they started by securing the cellars and building air raid shelters there. During the Second World War an additional massive aboveground air raid bunker was erected for the Reich Security Main Office. Air raid protection ditches were also dug on the site, in one of which many inmates from Sachsenhausen concentration camp were killed during the bombing in spring 1944.

The bunker was blown up in 1954.

During construction measures in 1996, workers discovered the entrance staircase, an anteroom with an air raid shelter door and ca. 17 m of an originally concrete-roofed split trench.

The present-day path runs parallel to the former air raid protection ditch.

Plans for the construction of several air raid shelters in the basement of Gestapo headquarters, August 1933.

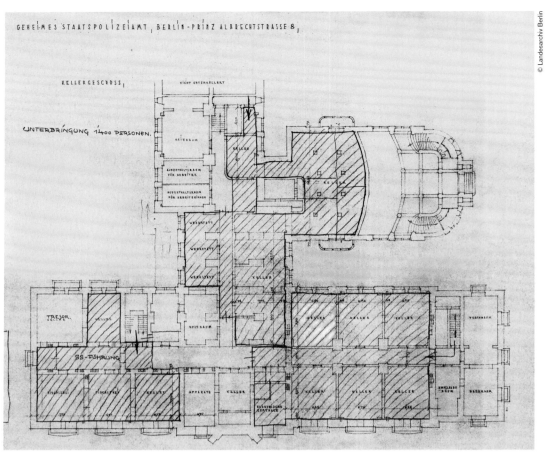

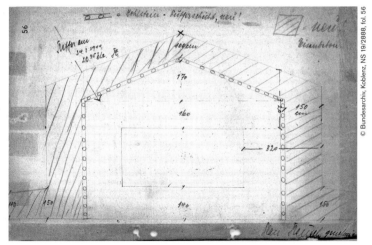

Sketch of the Reich Security Main Office air raid bunker after the bomb hit of March 24, 1944.

Members of the Technical Emergency Corps with gas masks on an exercise outside the Reich Aviation Ministry on "German Police Day," January 17, 1937.

Excavated zigzag-shaped air raid protection ditch
on the site of the Topography of Terror, spring 1997.

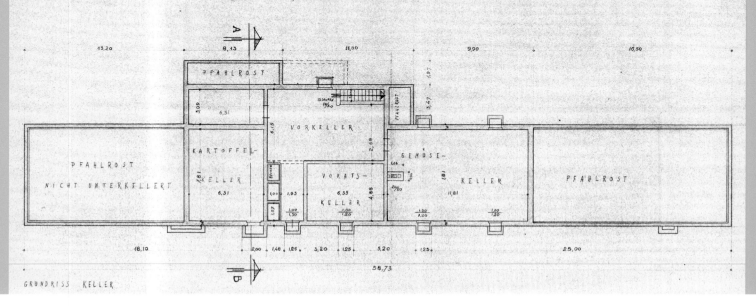

Unterkellerung Verpflegungsbaracke
für den pers. Stab des Reichsführers - ﬀ

1 " 100

PFAHLROST

PFAHLROST
NICHT UNTERKELLERT

KARTOFFEL-
KELLER
6,31

VORKELLER

VORRATS-
KELLER
6,35

GEMÜSE-
KELLER
11,81

PFAHLROST

GRUNDRISS KELLER

Architectural drawing of the basement of the
SS mess hut, September 1942.

14 SS MESS HUT

In 1942/43, an additional canteen for members of the Reich SS Leader's Personal Staff was erected behind Gestapo head-quarters. The hut constructed by prisoners from Sachsenhausen concentration camp was located directly behind the prison yard, on one of the paths laid out by Lenné in the Prinz Albrecht gardens. This path ended at a garden wall, to which the gate that still exists today was probably only added in the Nazi period.

It is unclear whether the wooden hut already burned down during the war or was only torn down afterwards. All that remained after 1945 were the chimney and the cellar rooms.

The cellar rooms were discovered in 1987 during the building of the Topography of Terror exhibition hall. It was dismantled in 1997 with the beginning of construction on the Zumthor building, whose realization was halted in 2004. The Topography of Terror Documentation Center designed by Wilms/Hallmann opened in May 2010.

"Let's Dig" action on the former Gestapo site, initiated by the Active Museum Association and the Berlin History Workshop, May 5, 1985.

The Topography of Terror exhibition hall built on top of the basement of the former SS mess hut, 1989. At right, the protective roof over the remaining foundations of the Gestapo "house prison."

The construction sign for the new building project based on the winning design by Swiss architect Peter Zumthor has been unveiled, May 8, 1995.

Winning design for the Topography of Terror
Documentation Center by the architect Ursula Wilms
(Heinle, Wischer und Partner, Berlin) and the
landscape architect Prof. Heinz W. Hallmann (Aachen),
January 2006.

Rear view of the former Gestapo headquarters from the south, 1953. In front of the building at left is the wall of the prison yard with the remains of screens, before it the chimney of the former SS mess hut, at right the collapsed air raid bunker.

15 THE "HOUSE PRISON" AT GESTAPO HEADQUARTERS

Memorial

In the summer of 1933, the Gestapo set up a "house prison" in the basement of the southern wing of Prinz Albrecht Straße 8. In all, some 15,000 political opponents of the Nazi regime were held here up to the end of the war. Interrogations, often under torture, took place on the upper floors. Several prisoners committed suicide. Most prisoners were turned over to the judicial system and sentenced to a penitentiary or to death, but many were also transported directly to concentration camps.

The former Gestapo headquarters were partially demolished in 1953–54. The remainder was blown up in 1956.

In 1986, the remains of the "house prison" were discovered during measures to conserve traces of the site. Since 1988, the foundations of five cells have been preserved as a memorial and protected by a layer of sand. A gravel surface now marks the spot. The surviving traces also include fragments of the base of the prison yard wall.

Police photographs taken by the Gestapo, most of them
shortly after the arrest of the prisoners, 1935–1943.

The excavated foundations of several cells of the former Gestapo "house prison," September 1986. The wreathes mark 5 of a total of 20 cells in the southern cellblock.

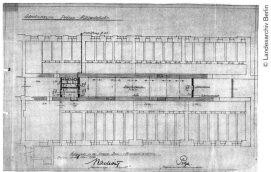

View of a solitary cell in the former "house prison," 1948. The cells were about 3.6 m long and between 1.4 and 1.7 m wide.

Drawing showing the expansion of the Gestapo "house prison" to include a second block of cells in the northern portion of the southern wing, May 1936.

HEADQUARTERS OF THE NAZI SS AND POLICE STATE

BUILDING USE AND CONSTRUCTION PLANS IN BERLIN

Construction and Planning in Nazi-era Berlin

It is quite clear, from contemporary speeches and publications of the Nazi period about completed and planned structures, that the Nazi regime considered architecture and urban development to be outstanding elements in the attempt to project its self-image and to demonstrate its power to the outside world. But which institutions and administrative bodies managed to achieve this goal and what was the relationship between the planning and realization of new buildings, the use of existing sites, and the treatment of available building stock? This essay explores these questions, focusing on the creation and expansion of SS and police headquarters in Berlin.

During the first years after the Nazis seized power, as in Munich, the "capital of the movement," and Nuremberg, the "city of the Reichsparteitage" (Nazi Party conventions), planning and construction in Berlin was limited to a series of larger building projects. These projects did not form part of an overarching plan; however, they were undeniably effective propagandistic tools. The first of the large construction projects in Berlin was the extension of the Reichsbank in the city center, begun as early as 1934, followed in 1935–36 by the monumental construction of the Reich Aviation Ministry on Wilhelmstraße. Construction on Berlin-Tempelhof Central Airport began in late 1935; already in 1934, work had started on the "Reichssportfeld," the massive Olympic sports facility in Charlottenburg. The trade fair halls, exhibition buildings, and "hall of honor" were built between 1934 and 1936 near the radio tower (Funkturm), while the "Deutschlandhalle" was going up nearby at the same time.

For the Nazi government, the "official seizure" of the traditional Prussian-German government quarter, and thus the use of existing buildings, was of crucial importance. It meant that, following the seizure of power, the traditional ministries remained in their palaces on Wilhelmstraße while new state and party authorities moved in nearby. Very few new buildings were added: Up to the beginning of the war, in addition to Hermann Göring's Reich Aviation Ministry, the only new structures were the extensions for Joseph Goebbels' Reich Propaganda Ministry in 1937–38, and Adolf Hitler's New Reich Chancellery in 1938–39. By 1937, with the creation of Albert Speer's new agency, the General Building Inspectorate for the Reich Capital (Generalbauinspektor für die Reichshauptstadt), and the "law on the redesign of German cities," the way had been paved for construction work on an unprecedented scale. The realization of plans to expand the capital into a huge power center – the future "Germania" as the metropolis of a greater Germanic Reich – meant the demolition of entire streets (already begun in 1938) and thus the partial destruction of several Berlin districts.

Just to the south of the government quarter was the area where the headquarters of the Nazi SS and Police State were located between 1933 and 1945. The 1987 opening of the exhibition "Topography of Terror" as part of celebrations marking Berlin's 750th anniversary and the historical documentation of the excavated traces of buildings on the site drew public attention to a recent past forgotten since the end of the war. An accurate picture of the creation and expansion of the headquarters of Nazi terror at this location can be drawn with the help of numerous documents from the Federal and State Archives in Berlin, as well as from testimonies by eyewitnesses. The Secret State Police (Gestapo) and SS not only occupied almost all the buildings on the Prinz-Albrecht-/Wilhelmstraße site, but also undertook a series of building alterations and set up several temporary structures. In addition, ambitious plans were developed for central office buildings, some of which were to be built on the site, others along Berlin's north-south axis planned by Speer. Compared to Hermann Göring's growing empire – which included the two buildings of the former Prussian Diet and the new Reich Aviation Ministry nearby –, Heinrich Himmler's power center across the street was, in terms of actual size and projected expansion, hardly less impressive.

SS and Police on the Prinz-Albrecht-/Wilhelmstraße Site

When they took up residence in the buildings on Prinz-Albrecht-/Wilhelmstraße, the Gestapo and SS confronted different historical structures. The first of the large buildings on the site was the palace of Baron François Matthieu Vernezobre de Laurieux, built during the rule of the "Soldier King" Friedrich Wilhelm I. Given the king's wish to lend "his" Berlin a more regal character, the wealthy baron undertook to construct a magnificent palace on the French model in 1737: a combination of a residential building with a courtyard and administrative and housekeeping wings unique in Berlin during this period. The construction of this palace extended the axis of noble town houses situated on the northern end of Wilhelmstraße southward; this southern segment was an area still marked by a more simple, rural character. For quite a while, this idyll remained undisturbed, and the garden – which Peter Joseph Lenné redesigned around 1830 and extended into a park – was "improved" during Karl Friedrich Schinkel's remodeling of the palace for Prince Albrecht of Prussia. One of Berlin's most impressive parks, its "portrait" has been painted many times, most notably by the artist Adolph von Menzel.

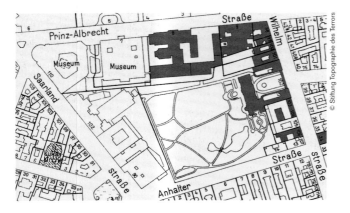

The headquarters of the Gestapo
and SS, site plan, 1938.

South wing of the former School of Industrial
Arts and Crafts, Prinz-Albrecht-Straße 8, 1931.

After Berlin became the capital of the newly founded German Empire in 1871, the city's ascent gathered breathtaking speed with the addition of numerous new streets and buildings. Included in this development was the area around Prinz Albrecht Palais; there was even some thought of creating a second "Museum Island" there. In 1881, the Museum of Industrial Arts and Crafts – today the Martin-Gropius-Bau – opened, followed five years later by the neighboring Ethnological Museum. In 1888 the Hotel Römerbad, later renamed Hotel Prinz Albrecht, was added; and in 1905, the School of Industrial Arts and Crafts opened as an "extension" of the Museum of Industrial Arts and Crafts. Within a few years, several imposing public buildings went up here, including the Prussian House of Representatives across the street. Wilhelmstraße, too, could be described as metropolitan: its two-storey, eighteenth-century buildings adjacent to the Prinz Albrecht Palais increasingly gave way to stately residential buildings of the Gründerzeit. The character of the district had already changed due to the new traffic centers at the Potsdamer and Anhalter train stations. Around the turn of the century, Prinz-Albrecht-Straße became a new thoroughfare after the Prussian War Ministry had dropped its opposition to cutting a street through its extensive gardens. Further development of the site did not resume until after World War I, with the Europahaus complex going up on the western side of Prinz Albrecht gardens beginning in 1926.

During the "Third Reich," the central institutions of Nazi terror were established in this district bounded by Prinz-Albrecht-, Wilhelm-, Anhalter- and Stresemannstraße (later: Saarland-straße): In April 1933, the newly established Prussian Secret State Police Office (Geheimes Staatspolizeiamt, or Gestapa) moved into the former School of Industrial Arts and Crafts at Prinz-Albrecht-Straße 8; one year later, Reich SS Leader Heinrich Himmler, in his new capacity as "Inspector" of the Secret State Police, took up offices there; joined in 1939 by the headquarters of the newly created Reich Security Main Office (Reichssicherheitshauptamt, or RSHA). In November 1934, the adjacent Hotel Prinz Albrecht became the headquarters of the Reich SS Leadership; and at about the same time, the Security Service (Sicherheitsdienst, or SD) of the SS, headed by Reinhard Heydrich, moved into Prinz Albrecht Palais at Wilhelm-straße 102. Subsequently, the Gestapo and SS also used almost all of the buildings adjacent to the palace along Wilhelmstraße for their burgeoning administration. But neither of the two museum buildings was used – they remained as museums – nor was the Europahaus complex, which initially continued to operate as a center with restaurants and entertainment and housed the Reich Ministry of Labor from 1939 on. Later it was briefly considered for inclusion in plans for the expansion of SS offices.

Even before 1933, the location was attractive for the Nazis. As early as the "Kampfzeit" (the "period of struggle," as the Nazis called the years before the seizure of power), the Nazi publisher "Der Angriff" (The Attack) bought the building at Wilhelmstraße 106, a prominent location close to Berlin's government quarter and just steps away from the city's press center.

The decision to house the newly established Secret State Police Office in the former School of Industrial Arts and Crafts came shortly after the seizure of power. Conditions were favorable: Since the relocation of the school to Charlottenburg in 1925, Prinz-Albrecht-Straße 8 had been rented out by a private company to various businesses, administrative agencies, and individual artists. When the temporary lease expired, the Prussian Finance Ministry transferred the property on April 1, 1933 to the internal administration. Still, the choice of the building at Prinz-Albrecht-Straße 8 for the newly founded Gestapa is surprising insofar as the idea of turning the building into a governmental authority had been rejected just a few years earlier on the grounds that the structure, especially designed as an art school, was unsuitable for governmental purposes. However, one crucial factor ruled in favor of using this building: Hermann Göring's construction of a personal power center with buildings within easy walking distance of one another. The proximity between the Gestapa and the Prussian Interior Minister and Minister President was to be made clear in spatial terms as well, through the selection of a site in the immediate vicinity of Göring's office and residence.

After the Gestapo moved into the former School of Industrial Arts and Crafts in the spring of 1933, there was no need to completely redesign the rooms and enough offices were available at that point. First, the Gestapo occupied part of the north wing of the building. One year later, the rooms of the art library and the hall housing the Lipperheidesche Kostümbibliothek (Costume Library) were added. In the late summer of 1933, the Gestapo had partitions put up in the former sculpture workshops in the south wing to create prison cells; in the summer of 1936 an additional wing of cells was added. The two-storey transversal wing constructed in 1911 by architect and school director Bruno Paul was turned into two canteens. The Gestapo's organizational chart for October 1935 reveals that all three main departments of the Secret State Police Office were still at Prinz-Albrecht-Straße 8. Himmler, Heydrich and the organizational and administrative department (Dept. I) had moved into the first floor; the Political Police (Dept. II) and Police Intelligence (Dept. III) took the second and third floors. The ground floor housed a driver service, a cashier's office, a medical services department, a part of the administrative department under Werner Best, and – as of late 1934 – the newly established "Inspectorate of Concentration Camps"

Ballroom of the Prinz Albrecht Palais after a design by K. F. Schinkel, ca. 1900.

Prinz Albrecht Palais (garden side), Wilhelmstraße 102, 1941–42.

headed by Theodor Eicke. But in the long run the building proved too small and by the summer of 1936 only Departments I and II were still housed there. The war brought additional changes in the allocation of rooms. Only portions of the now extensive Department IV (i.e., the Secret State Police Office) of the Reich Security Main Office were still located at Prinz-Albrecht-Straße 8. They included some of the sections dedicated to combating political opponents (IV A) and intelligence (IV E), while Adolf Eichmann's so-called "Juden-referat" (Jewish Affairs Section), IV B 4, for example, was housed at Kurfürstenstraße 115–116 – separately from other sections of the IV B group (ideological-racial opponents). But the headquarters of the Reich Security Main Office never moved from Prinz-Albrecht-Straße 8.

While a special state agency ever less subject to judicial control was established in the former School of Industrial Arts and Crafts, the former Hotel Prinz Albrecht became the "SS House" in autumn 1934, when Heinrich Himmler transferred the most important offices of the SS leadership from Munich to Berlin. Among them were the Adjutancy, from which the Personal Staff of the Reich SS Leader would later emerge; the SS Office, which later became the SS Main Office and represented the actual administrative seat of the SS; and the later Personnel Chancellery, which in 1939 would become the SS Personnel Main Office, including within its jurisdiction the personnel administration of the Waffen SS. In addition, the SS staff treasury, the auditing department and for a time the chief of telecommunications were housed in the Hotel Prinz Albrecht, which had been remodeled in 1909 in Art Nouveau style and was considered one of the more exclusive addresses during the Weimar Republic.

The most valuable nearby property that the SS rented from the Hohenzollern family was the Prinz Albrecht Palais on Wilhelmstraße. Quite early on, the Nazi Party had used it as an effective venue for events; it was here that the memorial exhibition dedicated to Leo Schlageter, which had originated in Düsseldorf, was shown in July 1933. Then, at the end of 1934, the Security Service of the SS moved into the palace, which offered not only office space but also dormitories for staff. Initially, Heinrich Himmler set his sights on setting up a "Museum of Freemasonry" in the Palais to display objects confiscated from the facilities of various Masonic lodges, which would then be presented to state and party leaders during their visit to the SD Main Office. During the war, the decision was made to convert the palace into the impressive head-quarters of the chief of the Reich Security Main Office. Reinhard Heydrich lived to see the remodeling completed, but probably never actually moved into his new official headquarters.

From the mid-1930s onward, almost all the buildings around Prinz Albrecht Palais (Wilhelmstraße 98–107) housed Gestapo and SS offices. In early 1936, the "Inspectorate of Concentration Camps" headed by Theodor Eicke moved from Prinz-Albrecht-Straße 8 to Wilhelmstraße 98 for a few months. Later, various Gestapo departments, including "Protective Custody" ("Schutz-haft") were housed here and in the neighboring building, no. 99. Additionally, the library of the RSHA occupied two rooms at Wilhelmstraße 99 during the war. Wilhelmstraße 101 housed Gestapo Intelligence (Abwehr) as well as some SD offices from 1936, while additional offices of the SS or RSHA were located at Wilhelmstraße 100, including parts of the SS Main Office as well as, temporarily, the chief of telecommunications. In addition to Prinz Albrecht Palais, the SD laid claim to the adjacent building at Wilhelmstraße 103–104 and later added the former "Angriff" building at Wilhelmstraße 106. The only buildings near the palace not used by the Gestapo and SS were Wilhelmstraße nos. 105 and 107. The former remained a private apartment building with many tenants and, given its poor structural conditions, was apparently never considered for use. In contrast, the Gestapo had approached the owner of the Hotel Wartburg on the corner of Wilhelmstraße 107/Anhalter Straße 13 several times by October 1936, proposing to rent or perhaps even buy the building prior to substantially reconfiguring it or replacing it with a new structure.

Alterations, Temporary Structures, and Air Raid Protection Measures

In order to accommodate the Gestapo and SS offices, alterations were planned or carried out over the course of time in most buildings on Prinz-Albrecht- and Wilhelmstraße, ranging from renovation and modernization to considerable structural alterations.

The expansion of the Gestapo "house prison" in the basement of the south wing of Prinz-Albrecht-Straße 8 has already been mentioned. It was initially established in 1933 with nineteen (later twenty) cells, a block of eighteen solitary cells and one communal cell added in 1936. Somewhat later an air raid shelter, which also served as a waiting room for prisoners, was added between the cellblocks. Extensive alterations were also undertaken at Wilhelmstraße 100, a building that the SS had rented to house additional offices. The intention in this case was to restore the building's façade to its pre-1877 condition, replacing two shops – for which the front windows had been altered – with a new room for guards, a common room and a waiting room. Far more extensive alterations were undertaken for the building adjacent to the Prinz Albrecht Palais, at Wilhelmstraße 103–104, which the SS also rented in 1934 at about the same time as they moved into the palace. Alterations were completed only a few months later, in July 1935, with many new offices in the front building and a block of dormitories for employees of the SS Security Service Main Office in the rear wing.

The Prinz Albrecht Palais was supposed to be transformed into an impressive headquarters for Reinhard Heydrich in 1941. By that time the former Palais Vernezobre had already borne the imprint of architect Karl Friedrich Schinkel for a century. From 1830 to 1832, Schinkel had carried out major alterations of this baroque structure at the behest of its new owner, Prince Albrecht of Prussia. They included a redesign of the street façade, with the addition of an arcade allowing a view of the palace. In the interior of the main building, Schinkel primarily extended the stairwell. While Schinkel dedicated the ground floor to the royal living quarters, the first floor was to be reserved for social events. Here Schinkel met his client's need for grandeur by expanding, redesigning and redecorating the magnificent oval marble hall, the two ballrooms – each encompassing more than 100 square meters – as well as the four banquet halls with buffet rooms and two galleries for musicians. In contrast, the second storey was furnished quite simply. It included about twenty-five relatively small rooms for aides and court servants.

Postwar photograph of the former Gestapo "house prison" with cells on the courtyard side (lower row of windows), 1948.

Photo: Norbert Leonard © Stiftung Topographie des Terrors

In 1934, the Prinz Albrecht Palais was occupied initially by various offices of the SS Security Service. To accommodate them, certain adjustments were made – such as new installations for heating, lighting as well as plumbing for sanitary facilities – which, though necessary, were undertaken with little regard for Schinkel's palace design; the condition of the wall and ceiling decorations deteriorated quickly. In March 1941, after Heydrich's decision as chief of the Reich Security Main Office to make the Prinz Albrecht Palais his headquarters, the structure was subjected to much-needed renovations. According to the building program, the first floor was to contain only Heydrich's offices and conference rooms; the upper mezzanine was to be expanded into offices; and the ground floor was to accommodate a mess hall, registries and a few rooms for advisors. But there was never any thought of completely restoring the palace in Schinkel's style. Rather – in the words of Friedrich Hetzelt, head of the Department of Public Works for Special Assignments – the "unified artistic approach" of the interrelated rooms on the upper floors was to be restored. At any rate, Schinkel's design and color scheme only survived relatively intact in the central oval room and in the two large halls as well as in the stairwell, because there had already been some alterations at the end of the nineteenth century. Hetzelt had the ceiling stuccowork simplified, walls rearranged and a new color scheme chosen, primarily in those rooms grouped around the main area. But alterations were also made to the large halls themselves. Art historian Johannes Sievers, who had a chance to visit the palace and see Schinkel's rooms in 1929, was shocked at the stylistic interventions by the Nazis. In his postwar book about the buildings of the Prussian princes, he called the marble hall "practically the chief victim." Intended to serve as Heydrich's office, its mirrored wall was replaced with a huge tapestry featuring a swastika. The side niches were walled up and half-height glass bookcases inserted into the lower sections, above which ran a grate in a fret pattern, presumably an outlet for air heating. Sievers also found the festive wall lighting in the ballroom to have been completely ruined; in its place hung shallow bowls encircled by upright metal leaves, "somebody's bright idea." And in the large dining hall it was the "folly of the architects" to dismantle a magnificent buffet designed by Schinkel and create various awkward-looking consoles from its parts.

Aside from the structural alterations to existing buildings, a few temporary structures of a more or less makeshift character also went up on the Prinz-Albrecht-/Wilhelmstraße site during the Nazi period. A large, two-storey garage wing was added in 1936 next to the main building of the Gestapo, which also included dormitories for drivers and rooms for the repair workshop responsible for all official Security Police vehicles. A wooden shed for part of the SD fleet had been put up early on at the boundary of the property at Wilhelmstraße 105–106. In 1937, building permits were issued not only for the construction of a one-storey garage here, but also for the conversion of a large part of the basement of Wilhelmstraße 106 into an underground garage. An additional temporary structure emerged in 1942/43, when another canteen building was built for members of the Reich SS Leader's Personal Staff – a wooden barrack resting partly on a pile foundation and partly on stone cellars, at the back of Gestapo headquarters, directly by the prison yard.

While numerous air raid protection measures were among the structural alterations on the Prinz-Albrecht-/Wilhelmstraße site – from the expansion of "shelters" to the safeguarding of the basements – the only massive concrete structure on the garden side of Prinz-Albrecht-Straße 8 was an aboveground air raid bunker built in 1941. It included Heinrich Himmler's command post as well as Ernst Kaltenbrunner's, and was reserved for higher-ranking staff of the Reich Security Main Office as well as for selected prisoners of the Gestapo "house prison."

New Construction Plans for the SS and Police Headquarters

With their claim to most of the buildings on the Prinz-Albrecht-/ Wilhelmstraße site, the Gestapo and SS had tried since 1934 to accommodate their growing need for office space. Although alterations were planned or actually undertaken on many buildings to that end, plans for the spatial expansion of the SS and police headquarters went much further – particularly since the increasing use of private homes did not present a satisfactory long-term solution.

Starting in the autumn of 1934, various plans were developed for expanding the space available to the Secret State Police Office. In October a design for a new Gestapo office building was presented in connection with plans for a garage wing: a three-storey front building intended to close the gap between the main building at Prinz-Albrecht-Straße 8 and the former Hotel Prinz Albrecht. But the project was postponed and only the garage complex was realized. Three years later, Albert Speer's agency discussed adopting an "interim solution" that Chief Building Officer Friedrich Hetzelt of the Department of Public Works for Special Assignments had proposed for a structure on the same site. "This new structure, like the existing buildings, could be used for other purposes later, after the construction of the new police building," Hans Stephan, Chief Building Officer at the General Building Inspectorate, reported to Albert Speer, who did not participate in this meeting. Not long afterwards, on October 6, 1937, Speer was present at another planning discussion, which is described in a memo by the Department of Public Works:

"Herr Professor Speer is shown the site plans for the extension of the Secret State Police Office building, as required by regulations. It is emphasized that the Secret State Police Office's need for space has become so urgent that an immediate closure of the gap between the Hotel Prinz-Albrecht and the former School of Industrial Arts and Crafts on Prinz-Albrecht-Straße is planned, through the construction of an extension. Herr Professor Speer explains that construction of a new Police Headquarters, which would also house the Secret State Police Office, is expected to be completed only in 1948, so that the necessity of implementing an extension for the 'Gestapo' is recognized in principle. But Herr Speer requests that general urban design considerations be emphasized in preparation of the proposed project, as set out in the sketches. There is unanimity with regard to the preference for a development project that does not envisage a simple closing of the gap between buildings along the street, but rather that emphasizes the existing character of Prinz-Albrecht-Straße. This can be achieved by development of the street with larger buildings not adjoining one another, such as is already the case with the Ethnological Museum, the Museum of Industrial Arts and Crafts, and the House of the Aviators (Haus der Flieger). Herr Professor Speer would lend his broadest support to a project that would take into consideration this understanding of urban development."

These plans for a building (already considered a mere "preliminary extension" of the Gestapa) were not realized, however, nor was there any evidence of the more or less concurrent plans to build a gigantic new structure on the entire site between Prinz-Albrecht-Straße 8 and the Prinz Albrecht Palais being implemented. The issue became increasingly important for Himmler after the beginning of the war in the autumn of 1939. In November he turned to Hermann Göring in his capacity as Commissioner for the Four-Year Plan and General Commissioner for the Regulation of the Construction Industry in connection with the construction plan. In reemphasizing the need for a new building, Himmler not only stressed the importance of the newly created Reich Security Main Office but also pointed out the constant new difficulties that would arise from the "spatial dispersal and separate accommodation of offices" – the Gestapa and the Main Office of the Security Police alone would be housed at seven different locations.

"That is why I commissioned the Department of Public Works for Special Assignments back in 1937 to draw up plans for construction of a new office building. The corner of Wilhelm-/Prinz-Albrecht-Str. was envisioned as the future site of such a building. The site presently is occupied by properties I have rented – properties that give an unattractive architectural impression. The planning, which reflected the urban outlook and intentions of the General Building Inspector and which he had expressly approved, was based on the idea, rather than simply closing the gap between buildings along the street, of actually adhering to the existing character of Prinz-Albrecht-Str. ... Properties at Prinz-Albrecht-Str. 8a (garage yard), Prinz-Albrecht-Str. 9 (Hotel Prinz-Albrecht) as well as Wilhelmstraße 98, 99, 100 and 101 are included in the planning. A six-floor office building with about 1,150 work spaces and the necessary special rooms is foreseen."

It was estimated that this building, intended for the Gestapo, would require a construction sum of 18 million Reichsmark. An additional building on the site was under consideration. Himmler commented on this "south building" as well:

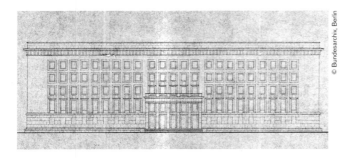

Preliminary sketch for the new office building of the Security Service of the SS (south building). The main entrance at Anhalter Straße, December 1938.

"Furthermore, a new office building containing a total of 569 work spaces on 8,900 sq.m of dedicated office space is to be built on the southern side of the Palais Prinz-Albrecht, which already is connected on its northern side to the stipulated building block. The two new structures are to form an organizational and architectural unit. Correspondingly, the new office building is to have six floors and reflect the style of Wilhelmstr."*

But these plans were not realized either, because neither Hermann Göring nor Albert Speer granted the necessary approval to requests that both new RSHA construction projects be declared vital to the war effort. The total cost of about 24 million Reichsmark and the need for raw materials – about 6,000 tons of construction steel – seemed too high.

Starting in the mid-1930s, plans for the centralization of SS and police offices included new construction not only on the Prinz-Albrecht-/Wilhelmstraße site but also on Albert Speer's planned north-south axis. Its approximately 7-km-long middle section was intended to be the real "grand boulevard" with the most important state and party buildings, showpieces of the leading corporations, an array of memorials and monuments as well as a triumphal arch on the transverse axis to Tempelhof Airport and, in the immediate proximity of the Reichstag building, the "Great Hall" as the Reich capital's "crowning glory." Hermann Göring's reaction after seeing Speer's plans for an immense Army High Command facility on the north-south axis shows just how coveted such a location was. Göring, as Commander in Chief of the Air Force, came to regard his spaciously laid out Aviation Ministry, just built in 1935–36 between Leipziger-, Wilhelm- and Prinz-Albrecht-Straße, as beneath his status and was able to win over the architect to plan a monumental structure for the Reichsmarschallamt on a central location on the axis: across from the "Soldatenhalle" (soldiers' memorial hall).

By the autumn of 1936 Heinrich Himmler had already contacted Speer, first with a request for a proposal for a uniform structure for "all central offices of the SS and police" on the Prinz-Albrecht-/Wilhelmstraße site. But in May 1937 the General Building Inspector for the Reich Capital was asked to report on whether the plans for the new government street also included an office building for the Reich SS Leader and Chief of the German Police. The answer was positive. A site located on the train yards of the Anhalter and Potsdamer stations was set aside

---

* In comparison: The Reich Aviation Ministry on Wilhelmstraße, completed in 1936, had 56,000 sq.m of floor space. The stipulated space allocation program encompassed 2,000 offices as well as numerous conference rooms and halls.

for the new office building – that is, within the north-south axis and close to the Prinz-Albrecht-/Wilhelmstraße site. Construction was not expected to be completed for another eight or ten years, however.

Plans for a new Gestapa building – instead of merely a "preliminary expansion" – also took on a new momentum in 1937. In addition to a plan for a large building on Wilhelmstraße north of the Prinz Albrecht Palais, a design was also commissioned for the north-south axis, which was now to be located on the connecting road to Tempelhof Airport. This project triggered additional plans and more concrete ideas in the form of three more buildings in addition to the new Gestapa building: one for the Reich SS Leader and Chief of the German Police on Yorckstraße, another for various SS offices on Immelmannstraße, and a third for the State Police Regional Office (Staatspolizei-leitstelle) Berlin near Tempelhof Airport. Finally, in February 1939, a clear solution emerged for the new Gestapa building, as Speer told the Chief of the Security Police, Reinhard Heydrich:

"Given the substantial expansion of your building for the Secret State Police Office on Prinz-Albrecht-, Wilhelm- and Anhalter Strasse, my proposed new Secret State Police Office building on a preferred urban site is obsolete."

In the same letter, Speer asked Heydrich to send him the designs for this building for approval. But in January 1940 hopes for a new Gestapa building as part of the expansion of the Reich Security Main Office had been finally dashed. Even Himmler's efforts that year to expand the offices, particularly into buildings near Prinz-Albrecht-Straße, met resistance. "It has not been possible thus far to provide the total required space, which, based on official standards, was estimated at about 50,975 sq.m, because the procurement of suitable office space in Berlin is posing nearly insurmountable difficulties," he complained to Speer's agency in September 1940. Speer's office also denied permission to turn the commercial space at Schützenstraße 15–17 into offices; in another case, the purchase of Linden-straße 51–53, permission to "redefine the use" of the building for offices was granted only on the condition that tenants be offered appropriate alternative accommodation and monetary compensation – a requirement that would greatly delay the takeover of the building.

Model of the north-south axis planned by Albert Speer in the area of the Runder Platz, planning as of 1940.

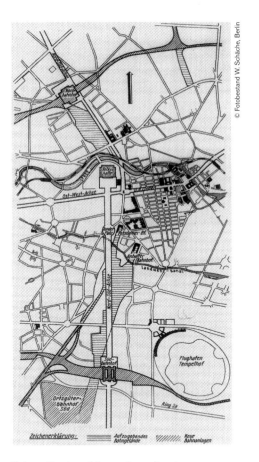

Schematic plan of the north-south axis between Nord- and Südbahnhof, 1937.

Himmler tried one more time to expand or centralize the SS offices. Again, the same two locations – the Prinz-Albrecht-/Wilhelmstraße site and the north-south axis – came under consideration, and on September 10, 1941 Himmler issued the following order to the SS Main Office for Budget and Buildings:

"1.) Examine the possibilities to include the buildings of the district around Prinz-Albrecht- and Saarlandstraße, including the Europahaus, for the purposes of a central office building for the Personal Staff;
2.) Prepare plans for a central building for all main offices, to be located on the north-south or east-west axis."

At this point, however, Speer's agency contemplated no change to the urban development plans for the Prinz-Albrecht-/Wilhelm-straße site and pushed instead for the protection of several buildings as historic landmarks, including the Prinz Albrecht Palais. And as far as the north-south axis was concerned, in no way did Speer want to turn this into a row of ministries and administrative buildings; rather, he wanted to reserve two thirds of the central section of the axis for private buildings and businesses. Thus in general there were no plans to build for party branch offices and other organizations, and even the government and administration structures were designed less to provide appropriate work spaces for staff than to symbolize the Reich's might and status.

But Heinrich Himmler remained in urgent need of surplus space, especially since the allocation of "Judenwohnungen" made available by Speer's agency hardly sufficed for the burgeoning SS offices, despite the doubling of this allocation in the first half of 1941 to 200 apartments, and the granting of a monthly quota of at least 50 rental permits later in the year.*

Two months later, on November 4, 1941, Oswald Pohl, chief of the SS Main Office for Budget and Buildings, received a letter that read in part:

"Since one cannot yet foresee how long the war will last, the question arises as to whether one could get to work on this with prisoners at a suitable location, at least for the most urgently needed construction, or whether it is more advisable to pursue the appropriate conversion of the district on Prinz-Albrecht-, Wilhelm- and Saarlandstr."

* After the November pogrom of 1938 ("Kristallnacht"), Speer's agency was already busy with the exploitation of the living quarters of Jews who had been expelled: so-called "Judenwohnungen." Starting in early 1941, Speer ordered the comprehensive evictions of Jewish tenants from their apartments so as to provide replacement apartments for people affected by demolitions in the course of the redesign of the capital.

With the increasing air raids on Berlin starting in 1943, the situation changed. Now, the dispersal of administrative offices was not only desired, but also actively pursued in the direction of decentralization. In addition, Himmler had ordered that all important card files and documents be stored outside Berlin; many alternative quarters for the SS main offices were created outside the city. By November 1943, after most of the buildings on Prinz-Albrecht- and Wilhelmstraße had either been damaged or destroyed during air raids, further plans for the expansion of an office building for the Reich SS Leader's Personal Staff were already drawn up for after the war. Thus a representative of the SS Main Office for Economy and Administration charged with developing the concept wrote to the Main Office of the Personal Staff on January 7, 1944 with a request for answers to the following questions:

"1.) How much space will the Personal Staff need after the war? …
2.) Has the Reich Leader already expressed any special wishes for the state rooms?
3.) In the large space within the city block, where the old tree stock of Prinz Albrecht gardens should be preserved wherever possible, the opportunity arises for designing a court or square of honor, connected with an open space that I can picture as a mixture between a rally ground, a parade ground, and a sports field.
4.) Has the Reich SS Leader said anything about whether a larger-than-average officers' mess is planned, whose state rooms approximate the reception rooms of the ministries?
5.) Do you think it is correct to plan for living spaces and guest rooms within the entire building complex as well, along the lines of a middle-sized hotel, especially given that there will be a great deal of traffic between the decentralized administrative offices?"

Reasons for the Failure of the Building Projects

Given the various plans developed since the mid-1930s for construction of new central office buildings for the SS and police, the question inevitably arises as to why all efforts toward realizing these plans failed, resulting in the continued use of existing buildings on Prinz-Albrecht- and Wilhelmstraße. Was it a question of power, of financing, or of unclear lines of responsibility?

In the autumn of 1936, Heinrich Himmler presented the following suggestion to Albert Speer:

"On the occasion of a talk that I presented to the Führer about this site and the accommodation of the police, the Führer asked me to submit a proposal for the creation of a single new construction on this site which could house all central offices of the SS and police in an appropriate and dignified manner."

One year later, plans were discussed in Speer's agency. Himmler dropped his direct reference to Hitler (as did Best and Heydrich) in the letters that followed to Speer, whose position had fundamentally changed during this period: On January 30, 1937, Speer's high level planning agency was officially established; similar to a ministry, it was directly subordinate to Hitler. By the end of 1938, preparations had already begun on several sites, with much propagandistic fanfare, for the architectural "reshaping" of Berlin. But the full extent of this reshaping was to remain deliberately hidden from the public in order to avoid provoking questions about its financing.

The summer of 1939 saw the greatest chances for a new Gestapa building on Prinz-Albrecht-Straße, and the most concrete preparations. Speer had agreed in June that those tenants who had been forcibly evicted because of the new construction would receive substitute housing from the allocation of "Judenwohnungen"; in addition, they were treated as "demolition tenants" due to the restructuring work. But the Reich Ministry of Finance had indicated that it could not take a position on the expansion as long as there was no decision by the "Führer" to move all sections of the Reich Ministry of the Interior to the Regierungsstraße (government road). Speer then told the Chief of the Reich SS Leader's Personal Staff Karl Wolff that "the Führer had not yet made a final decision about the government buildings on the north-south axis, since construction on this project is not expected to begin before 1945." "But I have noticed that there is no intention to locate the Security Police administrative building within these government structures." In other words, the plans to "reshape" Berlin posed no obstacle to a new building on the Prinz-Albrecht-/Wilhelmstraße site. But in fact there were other counterarguments, and Speer outlined them in the same letter:

"... the current situation regarding labor supply requires the advancement and completion of construction already under way. The Führer has thus ordered, as per his decree dated July 17, 1939, that in the future, only the most important building projects for the reshaping of the Reich capital should be started. Since your planned construction project, encompassing the administrative building of the Secret State Police and the State Police Regional Office, is initially not decisive for my meeting the deadline regarding the reshaping of the Reich capital, I would only be capable of granting permission for the start of construction on the above-mentioned project if you could verifiably provide construction workers from outside."

With his diplomatic skills, Speer had avoided a direct rejection. Since 1937 there had already been a restricted allocation of steel and concrete for the benefit of "buildings vital to the war effort." The decree of July 17, 1939 added an absolute priority for the buildings for the north-south axis, which exacerbated the shortage of workers, so that the prospect of receiving construction permits became even more remote. Furthermore, applications for building permits could also be moved back and forth between the various administrative bodies involved in the process in order to avoid a clear decision. Thus the next attempt at new construction on the Prinz-Albrecht-/Wilhelmstraße site – leaving aside the general construction freeze imposed at the start of the war – ultimately remained bogged down. In early 1940, Göring's office (Commissioner for the Four-Year Plan) wrote to the General Building Inspector that the Reich SS Leader and Chief of the German Police had applied to him "to declare the new construction of the Reich Security Main Office as vital to the war effort" and sent the matter "for a decision at your convenience." But "given the current situation in the construction market" he did not consider "the initiation of such a large office building project" to be appropriate. Speer then wrote to the Reich SS Leader and Chief of the German Police:

"I can only approve your request to declare the planned new construction as vital to the war effort if the necessary amount of iron is available. Since the Prussian Finance Minister currently reports that this is not the case, I must ask you first to get in touch with the Prussian Finance Minister."

We do not know whether Himmler ever did so. At any rate, the "agreement" of November 27, 1939 clearly left the decision about approval of building projects within the bailiwick of the General Building Inspector.

Thus Speer consistently evaded, or was hostile towards, the wishes of the Reich SS Leader and Chief of the German Police for new buildings. His own projects, in contrast, remained practically unaffected by the reduction or even cessation of

New building for the Ministry of Propaganda,
postcard, undated.

The New Reich Chancellery, 1939.

construction at the start of the war. Despite the General Building Inspector's assumption of "special tasks vital to the war effort" (including construction of military installations and bunkers), Speer had soon managed to establish exemptions for his own projects. After the military victory over France in June 1940, work on the "reshaping" of Berlin could be resumed and in mid-April 1941 Speer finalized an "Immediate Action Program of the Führer" for further expansion of the seat of power on the north-south axis, for which Göring provided the funds.

The General Building Inspector appeared, to his contemporaries as well, as an obstacle to other building projects in the city. At the same time, Speer depended on cooperation with other offices – and so even before the war he initiated a close working relationship with Himmler, resulting in the SS being among the privileged recipients of rental permits from Speer's quota of "Judenwohnungen" in 1941.

While earlier plans for the expansion of the SS and police headquarters were developed in the Department of Public Works for Special Assignments or in Speer's agency, and had been discussed, Himmler's later plans for a structural expansion of his offices in the autumn of 1941 (intended to be carried out during the war) or of the Main Office of the Reich SS Leader's Personal Staff in January 1944 (intended for after the war), were prepared in the SS Main Offices for Budget and Buildings or Economy and Administration. The founding of this department, one of the largest SS main offices, on February 1, 1942 supported the intention to end the dependency of SS construction on the Reich's building administration and thus on the Reich Ministry of Finance, and instead to establish its own construction sovereignty, administer its own construction quotas, and also to concentrate all questions related to postwar SS and police construction in its own hands, independent of governmental agencies. But in the end these goals could not be met. Ultimately, in June 1944, Albert Speer placed all Reich building and construction work under the jurisdiction of "Organisation Todt," which he headed – and this affected SS building projects as well.

Concluding Remarks

A survey of all developments related to the creation and expansion of SS and police headquarters on the Prinz-Albrecht-/Wilhelm-straße site during the Nazi period leads to the conclusion that a power center gradually took root on a site already occupied by impressive buildings in the immediate vicinity of the government quarter, and that it functioned as the centerpiece of a much larger, city-wide network of administrative offices. Despite sustained, to some extent promising efforts, no new buildings were constructed, although various plans were developed and discussed, some of which envisaged radical alterations – up to and including demolition of the former Hotel Prinz Albrecht as well as all the existing residential buildings on Wilhelm- and Anhalter Straße. However, structural alterations were undertaken in almost all buildings used by the Gestapo and SS, not least in the Prinz Albrecht Palais, which in 1941/42 was turned into an imposing headquarters for Reinhard Heydrich. In addition, a few temporary structures were erected, primarily garage facilities, as well as a massive aboveground air raid bunker for the Reich Security Main Office. Thus in the vicinity of the Prinz-Albrecht-/Wilhelmstraße site, new construction stopped at the three large buildings for the Nazi leadership from the prewar period: Göring's Reich Aviation Ministry on the corner of Wilhelmstraße/Leipziger Straße, designed by architect Ernst Sagebiel in 1935–36, and for which the former Prussian War Ministry (among other buildings) had been torn down; the extensions that Goebbels demanded for the Reich Propaganda Ministry, built in 1937–38 according to the design of Karl Reichle, and for which the former Colonial Office (and other buildings) had to give way; and Hitler's New Reich Chancellery on Voßstraße 1–19, designed by Albert Speer and built in 1938–39 in only ten months, also requiring the demolition of existing buildings. No large structures for the headquarters of the Nazi SS and police state were ever built on the Prinz-Albrecht-/Wilhelmstraße site or as part of Speer's planned north-south axis.

The Reich Aviation Ministry, postcard, undated (ca. 1937).

The present contribution is the revised version of an essay by Erika Bucholtz, published in the Zeitschrift für Geschichtswissenschaft in 2004. For complete source notes and bibliography, see the original version. The sources consulted by the author include the following documents from the Bundesarchiv, Berlin: R 58 (Reichssicherheitshauptamt); NS 19 (Persönlicher Stab Reichsführer-SS); R 4606 (Generalbauinspektor für die Reichshauptstadt); as well as the Landesarchiv Berlin: B Rep. 206 (Baupolizei); A Pr.Br. Rep. 042 (Preußische Bau- und Finanzdirektion).

EYEWITNESS ACCOUNTS

Prinz-Albrecht-Straße 8, headquarters of the Secret State Police Office from 1933, and during the Second World War of the Reich Security Main Office as well, was not merely the place where the Schreibtischtäter, the bureaucratic organizers of Nazi crimes, had their offices. It was also a site of actual terror. Soon after the Gestapo headquarters moved into the building, a "house prison" was set up in its southern wing. Between 1933 and 1945 a total of some 15,000 political opponents of the Nazi regime were held for days, weeks or months in this "police custody of a very particular kind" (Reinhard Heydrich). They were mainly persons whom the Gestapo was particularly interested in interrogating. Up until 1939 most of them were members of banned political parties and the resistance groups that grew out of them, and during the war years especially of the new resistance circles, the "Red Orchestra" (Rote Kapelle) and the "20th of July." Many prisoners were tortured, and several were driven to suicide. Prinz-Albrecht-Straße 8 had become an address to be feared.

The following recollections of former inmates describe their detention in the Gestapo "house prison." Also included here are two accounts by family members of prisoners, which describe their impressions upon entering Gestapo headquarters at Prinz-Albrecht-Straße 8. Two accounts come from former prisoners of Sachsenhausen concentration camp who were detailed to do forced labor on the grounds of the Reich Security Main Office. The final two excerpts relay the impressions and feelings of former prisoners and their friends when they revisited the ruins of Gestapo headquarters after the war.

© Gedenkstätte Deutscher Widerstand, Berlin

Clara Harnack, mother of Arvid and Falk Harnack, outside the main entrance to the former Gestapo headquarters, Prinz-Albrecht-Straße 8, 1945.

Family Members of Prisoners at Gestapo Headquarters

Falk Harnack (1913–1991),
undated.

Dr. Falk Harnack received permission to visit his brother Arvid Harnack (1901–1942) at Prinz-Albrecht-Straße 8 twice in 1942. As a central figure in the "Red Orchestra" resistance group, Arvid Harnack had been arrested in September 1942 and detained at the Gestapo "house prison." Three months later, he was executed at Plötzensee Prison in Berlin. Falk Harnack, who had close ties to resistance circles himself, wrote an account immediately after his second visit and expanded it in 1983. His recollections also describe the situation he encountered upon entering Gestapo headquarters.

Christabel Bielenberg (1909–2003),
undated.

Christabel Bielenberg reported voluntarily to give a statement to exonerate her husband, who had been arrested in connection with the July 20th conspiracy. In an account of her years in Germany, which appeared in 1968, Bielenberg describes the interrogation at Prinz-Albrecht-Straße on January 4, 1945 and her impressions upon entering Gestapo headquarters.

An armed SS sentry stood at the main portal. I had to tell him that I was expected, and whom I wanted to see. He simply nodded, and I pushed a doorbell. Then it buzzed and the door opened. When I had entered the small anteroom the door fell to behind me, without a handle. When you entered this building – I do not wish to exaggerate – you did so with great trepidation, because you never knew whether you would leave again. I always had a young man accompany me. I gave him all of my valuables, and he had to wait in a nearby restaurant. If I did not return after two hours he was to sound the alarm. Standing in the anteroom, I approached a small porter's window, behind which sat a man in SS uniform. He asked for my papers and the name of the Gestapo officer I was going to see. Then I received a visitor's card. The porter pushed another button, it buzzed again, and after walking through the big door I found myself in the huge stairwell. A very bombastic, broad flight of stairs led up to the first floor, and to its left and right rose stairs to the other floors. I saw no other people, but felt sure I was being watched from somewhere. So I went up to the first floor.

The headquarters of the Gestapo in the Prinz Albrechtstrasse I found to be a huge, gloomy edifice partly destroyed by bombs. As I climbed the wide stone steps I realized that I had made one mistake in my eagerness to play the part. My coat was made of synthetic wool, a new discovery since the war, material made from wood. It looked like wool and felt like wool and might have been cotton netting for all the warmth it provided. I began to shiver a little as I paused at the top of those wide stone steps. … I shivered again and hurried inside. A mild-faced porter came out of his Office and asked me what I wanted. Room 525, Herr Kriminalrat Lange. He told me to go up the stone staircase to the third floor, along the passage and that it was the fourth door on the left.

When I reached the third floor I was out of breath and numb with cold. My knees were knocking together and my hand on the marble banisters was shaking as if with ague. At each floor, I passed the padlocked doors of a huge lift shaft, which descended into the darkness of the cellars. The atmosphere of the place was horrifying, silent, echoing and cold, deathly cold. A long dimly lit corridor stretched out ahead of me, No 527, No 526, No 525 Vorzimmer Kriminalrat Lange. I knocked at the door and after a short wait the door was opened by a uniformed SS man.

Falk Harnack, in Johannes Tuchel and Reinold Schattenfroh, Zentrale des Terrors. Prinz-Albrecht-Straße 8: Hauptquartier der Gestapo, Berlin 1987, p. 239.

Christabel Bielenberg, The Past is Myself, London 1968, reprint 1989, p. 229.

Recollections of Detention at the Gestapo "House Prison"

Edith Walz was among the detainees delivered to the newly established Gestapo "house prison" during the first year of its existence. The twenty-two year old legal assistant was arrested on December 6, 1933 and released after one week, since there was no evidence against her. Walz, who belonged to a small resistance group within a socialist youth organization and participated in leafleting actions, described her interrogation during a 1990 interview.

Edith Walz (1911–2004), 1929.

Georg Thomas, head of the Office of Defense Economy and Armaments in the Armed Forces High Command until November 1942 and in contact with the military opposition since 1938, was taken into custody in connection with the series of arrests after July 20, 1944. He survived Flossenbürg and Dachau concentration camps and died in 1946 in American custody. He reported on his several months at the Gestapo "house prison," which began in October 1944, in an account written after the war.

Georg Thomas (1890–1946), ca. 1940.

Then a man in uniform – I am one hundred percent certain he was in uniform, that horrible SS uniform – accused me of being obdurate. He said, "So, now we're going to show you what to expect if you keep acting this way," or something to that effect. They took me down to the cellar, and that was the most horrific experience, which will stay with me for the rest of my life. …

When we got downstairs he ordered – all they did there was shout, after all, the people there were sub-humans – "Everybody stand in front of the windows" or something like that. And then he led me down the corridor from cell to cell past these windows, with those completely beaten up faces. No, … you never forget those images, ever. And those completely beaten up faces. Everything was still new to me but because that trauma has never left me, and I have dealt with all these things and events my whole life long, because I never understood what people are capable of. Even today I am still trying to fathom how a human being is capable of that. To look into those faces, completely beaten up, faces that were no longer faces at all, and then go upstairs again, and then the man said to me, "If you persist in your obdurate behavior the same thing will happen to you. We can do it – You may still be young" or "a girl," perhaps they said that as a form of excuse, I don't know, "but you will look just like that." … Of course I was completely downcast, completely beaten down, but even then there was this awareness in me that not a word had yet been said about what they knew.

I was held in solitary confinement in a basement cell. During the day the bed had to be tipped up against the wall; in the daytime it could only be used from 1230–1330 hours. A chair and a little table made up the rest of the furnishings. There was neither a cupboard nor any other place to put things. They had taken away my suitcase, reading matter, medicines, etc. The midday rations were tolerable under the circumstances, but very meager. … The sub-officers deployed especially to guard the political prisoners varied greatly. Some of them behaved quite properly and themselves complained about the system. Others were genuine sadists and tormentors. They took special pleasure in harassing you with the smallest things. The main point for them was to treat you as disrespectfully as possible. All those who had already been sentenced to death were shackled day and night, as were some of the inmates who were still undergoing interrogation. I was only shackled the night the building caught fire during a bombing raid. During air raids "prisoners of interest" were taken to the bunker, while others were locked in their cells, shackled hand and foot, and still others were locked in a large cellar room. With the Gestapo there was no "free hour" to get some fresh air. Torture was an everyday occurrence.

Edith Walz in an interview with Andreas Sander (Stiftung Topographie des Terrors), Berlin 1990.

Georg Thomas, in Johannes Tuchel and Reinold Schattenfroh, Zentrale des Terrors. Prinz-Albrecht-Straße 8: Hauptquartier der Gestapo, Berlin 1987, p. 283.

Johann Adolf Graf von Kielmansegg, from 1940 on the General Staff of the Army High Command, had connections to the military opposition. He was arrested in early August 1944 on suspicion of participation in the attempted assassination of Hitler on July 20. Since no direct involvement could be proven, he was released after six weeks. In 1997 Graf von Kielmansegg, Supreme Commander of the NATO land forces in the 1960s, spoke in an interview about his time as an inmate of the Gestapo "house prison" and about the treatment of prisoners during the frequent air raid alarms.

Johann Adolf Graf von Kielmansegg (1906–2006), summer 1942.

The only real change in the routine of the cruelly creeping minutes was the air raid alarm, which returned almost nightly. I and most likely the other inmates as well were the only people in all of Germany who looked forward to the air raids in a certain way, which may sound a bit cynical at first. When the air raid warning sounded we had to get up, dress, and wait in the dark, for then, and only then, were the lights turned off. Otherwise the bulb screwed over the door in the cell burned all the time, and it was a regulation that you had to sleep with your face towards the light, that is, on your back. …

When the main alarm sounded, the majority of the prisoners had to walk in pairs into the anteroom beyond the corridors, after they had been locked – that was the term for shackled, they always said locked, after they had been shackled, if they weren't already handcuffed in their cells. … We were probably selected according to how important individual inmates were for the Gestapo, and whose lives were somehow considered valuable. The rest were left to their fate in the cells, where they had little protection, since the cellar was not very deep underground. …

And this was the moment I always longed for the most. You went up a little staircase, past the kitchen, and then walked six steps, flanked by four to six SD men with machine guns, across the courtyard to a big concrete bunker. At that moment you saw the sky, which as I said was what I longed for the most. …

The bunker had been built for the higher Gestapo leaders and their staff, it contained an anteroom, a low, narrow hallway and four or five small rooms off this hallway, a bit like a sleeping car; that is how I remember it when I see it in my mind. Now I don't know whether there were two hallways, because we were always only in the one – of course there might have been a parallel corridor – but we went down the one on the left. We had to stand along the walls in the hallway, always one prisoner and one officer alternating so we couldn't talk to one another or pass each other anything. That is where you saw who was new and who was missing. The people I knew whom I met down there included Goerdeler and the Prussian finance minister Popitz, Schacht, the former ambassadors Graf von der Schulenburg and Hassel, General von Stülpnagel, who had shot and blinded himself, and his deputy chief of staff from France Colonel Fink, General Fromm, Colonel Hahn, and many other officers I didn't know. Except for Schacht, all the ones I knew were executed. The name "cellar of death" is no exaggeration. Standing for so long in that hot, airless hallway was very exhausting and people frequently fainted. The only one regularly allowed to sit down in the anteroom to the hallway was Schulenburg.

There was a little radiator in the hallway, and whoever was lucky enough to stand in front of it at least had something to lean on. I will never forget how Ambassador von Hassel, having once managed to capture this dubious seat, saw an elderly gentlemen with a neat white goatee, whom I did not know, begin to sway on his feet. Hassel stood up in his striped prison uniform, and with his shackled hands offered the older man his seat with an inimitably chivalrous gesture, as if he were in some drawing room. The officers permitted it tacitly, as if they too sensed the breath of true culture and inner freedom that lay over this scene. I've never forgotten, I can still see that gesture of his. Aside from Hassel only Lehndorff and Goerdeler wore prison uniforms. They had been arrested outside Berlin. The others all had on military uniforms without medals or civilian dress, for example Fromm, whom Kaltenbrunner treated with striking courtesy. You see sometimes Kaltenbrunner also came into the bunker and then he always took Fromm, who was the only person he greeted, into a private room, one of the rooms off the hallway I mentioned. Goerdeler was also generally kept apart and was subject to special precautionary measures.

Johann Adolf Graf von Kielmansegg in an interview with Andreas Sander (Stiftung Topographie des Terrors), Bad Krozingen 1997.

Forced Labor on the Site of the Reich Security Main Office

Josef Müller (1898–1979), 1946.

During the war, the lawyer Dr. Josef Müller participated actively in the military resistance as an officer in the Office for Foreign Affairs/ Counterintelligence of the Armed Forces High Command and made contact with the Allies via the Vatican. He was arrested in April 1943. After the failed attempt to assassinate Hitler, his ties to the July 20th circles were revealed. More than four months of his imprisonment – from September 1944 on – were spent in the Gestapo "house prison." He survived Buchenwald, Flossenbürg, and Dachau concentration camps. After the war, he served simultaneously as minister of justice and deputy minister president in Bavaria. In his autobiography he also wrote about his time as a prisoner at Prinz-Albrecht-Straße 8.

Karl Pioch (1911–1996), 1968.

Karl Pioch was one of the prisoners of a labor commando from Sachsenhausen concentration camp who were deployed in 1942/43 to build a new SS mess behind Gestapo headquarters. Pioch, who was interned as a Communist and survived the death march from Sachsenhausen, recalls this time in his book "Nie im Abseits."

From my cell I frequently heard awful screams that came from a floor above mine and often lasted a long time, then turned into a whimper, then grew loud again, so that there could be no doubt as far as I was concerned: people were being badly maltreated up there. The screams were so awful that I thought it could only be torture. I myself did not experience this increased level of violence until I was taken to Flossenbürg concentration camp. But my hands were bound together all the time, and the inner side of the manacles was rough; every time I made a careless movement, the fine hairs on my wrists were rubbed away. It was particularly painful whenever I tried to get some sleep. I had to wear the manacles during meals, during interrogations, and the whole night as well. ...

Although I personally never revealed a single name, I can well understand how some of my fellow prisoners lost their nerve. That constant sensation of being hungry, being shackled day and night, the light that was deliberately focused to shine directly into the prisoner's face during the night – all this created constant pressure which was exacerbated by the interrogations that lasted for hours, and by the fear of direct physical abuse. Needless to say, since the war the SD officers have largely denied that torture was ever applied. But shortly after I was committed to the basement prison of the RSHA, I saw Julius Leber's flayed back, and the back of one of the generals I saw in the washroom was likewise covered with welts.

I worked for quite some time in a large commando, which we called "kitchen hut," on the grounds of the Reich Security Main Office on Prinz-Albrecht-Straße.

At times there were thirty or forty prisoners doing construction on a large hut that was supposed to house a kitchen and dining hall for the SS leadership. We long-time workers then did the necessary interior work, without going out of our way. This kind of work was hard to check, and the skilled workers were acting very busy.

One day I was building an exhaust shaft on the roof of the building and risked a glance over the wall into the prison yard of Gestapo headquarters. Naturally that was forbidden but I wanted to see who was being allowed to take a stroll in the yard.

On that day I saw only one slender prisoner. Somehow his walk was familiar. When he was halfway around the yard I recognized Heinrich Rau, our former commander from the 11th International Brigade! One year previously we had spent six months in the same prison in the South of France awaiting trial. The French judges had to acquit us. I felt joy and dismay, joy because Heinrich Rau was still alive, dismay because he was being held at Gestapo central headquarters and I could do nothing to help him.

Josef Müller, Bis zur letzten Konsequenz. Ein Leben für Frieden und Freiheit, Munich 1975, pp. 220, 226.

Karl Pioch, Nie im Abseits, Berlin (GDR) 1978, p. 133.

The machinist Rudolf Wunderlich
was a prisoner of Sachsenhausen's
sub-camp in the Berlin district of
Lichterfelde, from which he managed
to escape in June 1944. In a 1987
account he describes his deployment
on the grounds of the Reich Security
Main Office after an air raid on Berlin
in the spring of 1944.

Rudolf Wunderlich (1912–1988),
undated.

There was an air raid on Berlin on Sunday, May 7, 44
around 11 o'clock (?) that also affected the area of
Prinz-Albrecht-Straße.

A total of twenty-nine concentration camp prisoners were
killed in a zigzag trench on the grounds of the Prinz Albrecht
gardens and the Gestapo building. These twenty-nine
prisoners were members of the "Prinz-Albrecht-Str." labor
commando from the Sachsenhausen sub-camp on
Wismarer Straße in the Lichterfelde district of Berlin.

There was a simple zigzag trench in the gardens for the
concentration camp prisoners, but it provided very inadequate
protection. Next to it was a more solid zigzag trench covered
with concrete slabs that was used during the week by workmen
and civilian employees of the RSHA. On Sundays, however,
the concentration camp prisoners always used this somewhat
safer trench.

And on May 7, 1944 this trench took a direct hit. The result
was twenty-nine men dead and one severely injured.

The news only reached us at the sub-camp in the afternoon.
I can still remember this event quite well because when making
a count of the dead, wounded, and living the SS found a
discrepancy of two or three prisoners. Since this discrepancy
could not be cleared up on May 7, 44 and there was a suspicion
that the "missing" prisoners had used the confusion after the
air raid to make an escape, on Monday, May 8, 44, a group of
ten German political prisoners were sent to the Reich Security
Main Office on Prinz-Albrecht-Straße to search the destroyed
trench, now filled with rubble, for bodies and body parts.
I belonged to that group of ten prisoners.

We found a few body parts among the rubble and in the ground.
In the afternoon, concentration camp prisoners found a few more
body parts during a renewed and thorough search of the RSHA
grounds, the partially damaged building of the Prinz Albrecht
Palais, and other adjacent partially damaged or destroyed
sections of buildings. Most of the buildings only had damage
to the windows. When the obviously large bomb (or were
there two?) exploded, the prisoners' body parts were flung
widely in the vicinity. This could be assumed or demonstrated
from the traces of blood on the trees in front of the Palais
and the buildings next to it.

It was a terrible day for us prisoners deployed to search.

Rudolf Wunderlich, manuscript, July 27, 1987
(Stiftung Topographie des Terrors).

The End of the Gestapo "House Prison"

© Willy Zahlbaum, Berlin

The bookkeeper Franz Lange was one of the last inmates in the "house prison" when it was liberated in May 1945. A few days before, the SS had shot several prisoners on a derelict site nearby. In 1966 Radio DDR broadcast an interview in which Lange, who had belonged to the Communist resistance and after the war worked for the GDR Ministry of Foreign Trade, described his final hours before being liberated.

Franz Lange (1904–1985), ca. 1946.

Around noon on May 1, we heard noises at the cell door. All of us inside stood facing the door. The door flew open and we were startled by a shout of "Out!" and chased down the stairs. On the stairs, the SS bumped off the German NCO who had been with us in the communal cell, and the other prisoners were locked in the former SS quarters. Everyone was lost in his own thoughts. I was convinced that only the Red Army could liberate us. Pastor Reinicke, for his part, found the strength to carry on through a prayer session that I, who had left the church at age 16, shall never forget. Towards afternoon, the turmoil inside the building increased. We heard noises and noticed that the SS was assembling. When an SS man asked his major what should be done with the prisoners locked inside, the major answered, "We're letting them live as proof that we don't shoot prisoners." And then they left. We were all by ourselves, alone in the huge building, which was almost completely destroyed. And we waited and waited and waited.

Waited all evening, all night until it was light again, and then on the morning of May 2, it might have been around 6 o'clock, we heard the sound of Russian. The Red Army entered the building. Their steps came closer. We hammered on the doors. Then the folding slot on the door was opened from the outside and we were met by a Russian word "kljuc" (key). My reply was "kljuc netu (there is no key). We are prisoners." It took only a few minutes, then axes crashed and the door flew open. I stood face to face with a young Red Army soldier. We were free.

Franz Lange, Deutsches Rundfunkarchiv, Potsdam-Babelsberg, recording of 1966.

The Ruins of Gestapo Headquarters

Photo: Juliette Lasserre © SZ Photo, München

In September 1948 the journalist Ursula von Kardorff visited the ruins of the former Gestapo headquarters with the photographer Norbert Leonard (1913–1971). The two of them had been at Prinz-Albrecht-Straße 8 during the Nazi period. Ursula von Kardorff had been called in for questioning in 1944 because she knew people connected with the July 20th circles, but was allowed to leave the building after several hours of interrogation. Norbert Leonard, categorized by the Nazis as a "Second Degree Mischling" (a "quarter Jew"), had been picked up carrying false papers in 1942 and detained at the Gestapo "house prison." The picture on p. 67 shows the cell in which he was imprisoned.

Ursula von Kardorff (1911–1988), 1950s.

We climb over detonated bunker walls, and stand in a narrow yard; the old Reich Aviation Ministry, now the headquarters of the Eastern Zone Administration, is visible through the splintered corrugated fence. At the side is a building with barred windows. We go inside, through vaults with bombed ceilings hanging down, past the elevator that looks like a coffin, and come to a long corridor. One opening after another – cells! One meter wide, three meters long. The heavy oak doors have doubtless long since gone for firewood. Everything has been cleared out, except the hooks for the folding beds. Piles of paper on the floor. So this is where they were imprisoned, men from every social class, every religion, from every province and abroad, men who were the regime's worst enemies. Shackled and abused. In anxious expectation, restless torment or calm resignation, despairing, rebellious, disheartened or brave. …

My companion took out his camera. Hesitantly, almost shuffling, he entered the cell. "Look – it's still here: scribbled in tiny pencilled letters, it was forbidden – it's still here, 'Take courage' – I wrote that," he said, overcome with emotion. The camera shook a bit in his hands. He had spent three months here in 1942, shackled to the bed at night.

Ursula von Kardorff, "Prinz-Albrecht-Straße". Ein gespenstischer Gang, Süddeutsche Zeitung, no. 86, Oct. 7, 1948.

The writer Günther Weisenborn belonged to the resistance group that the Gestapo called the "Red Orchestra" (Rote Kapelle). He was detained for several months at Prinz-Albrecht-Straße 8 from the autumn of 1942. Sentenced to three years in a penitentiary by the Reich Court Martial, he was liberated in 1945. In November 1950 Weisenborn visited the ruins of the former Gestapo headquarters with the writer Bertolt Brecht and the journalist Max Schroeder.

Günther Weisenborn (1902–1969), 1947.

It was very easy to get into the yard through a hole in the fence. A two-man sentry of stony SS members used to stand in front of the entrance. But I never went through the Prinz-Albrecht-Straße entrance. Back then I was driven into the yard in a van and taken to the basement where the cells were. When somebody bolted the door from outside, you felt the air pressure in your ears. It was the central headquarters of the Gestapo.

Now it was derelict. The floor of the first storey hung in the ruins like a blown-out tent. It was deathly still. Brecht and I turned first into the little yard where the so-called "walks" took place back then: six men, twenty minutes long, silence. Then we went into the waiting room, which used to have brown benches like church pews whose high sides were designed to prevent you talking secretly to your neighbor. I explained everything to him. I turned around, and will never forget the expression on Brecht's face, that kind of nearly scientific interest mingled with suppressed anger. We walked down the corridor and inspected the cells. They were empty. There was debris on the floor, shards, military relics, gas mask holders, empty cigarette packets, here and there a photo, a smudged leaflet. – We went into my former cell. I spent months here. It was very dark. "Was it always so dark?" "Yes." "Was it cold?" "Yes, but not as cold as in Spandau." The door was gone, chopped up for firewood. I could hardly see Brecht in the dark; he stood motionless like a shadow in my old, dilapidated cell. We stood motionless for a long time.

In width, the cell reached from the tip of my left hand to my right elbow, and was five paces long. How many prisoners had suffered here after me? I walked my old path, five paces back and forth. The rubble on the stone floor crunched under my shoes. When I stopped, it was deathly still.

Günther Weisenborn (r.) and Max Schroeder in the former prison yard of the Gestapo "house prison," November 1950.

Günther Weisenborn, Der gespaltene Horizont, Munich 1964, pp. 160–61.

A PRISON POEM
FROM THE GESTAPO "HOUSE PRISON"

DIETRICH BONHOEFFER

Dietrich Bonhoeffer (1906–1945), 1944 at Tegel Prison in Berlin.

"By Powers of Good"

By faithful, quiet powers of good surrounded
so wondrously consoled and sheltered here –
I wish to live these days with you in spirit
and with you enter into a new year.

The old year still would try our hearts to torment,
of evil times we still do bear the weight;
O Lord, do grant our souls, now terror-stricken,
salvation for which you did us create.

And should you offer us the cup of suffering,
though heavy, brimming full and bitter brand,
we'll thankfully accept it, never flinching,
from your good heart and your beloved hand.

But should you wish now once again to give us
the joys of this world and its glorious sun,
then we'll recall anew what past times brought us
and then our life belongs to you alone.

The candles you have brought into our darkness,
let them today be burning warm and bright,
and if it's possible, do reunite us!
We know your light is shining through the night.

When now the quiet deepens all around us,
O, let our ears that fullest sound amaze
of this, your world, invisibly expanding
as all your children sing high hymns of praise.

By powers of good so wondrously protected,
we wait with confidence, befall what may.
God is with us at night and in the morning
and oh, most certainly on each new day.

The Protestant theologian Dietrich Bonhoeffer, a leading member of the Confessing Church, was arrested in April 1943. From October 8, 1944 he was detained at Prinz-Albrecht-Straße 8, after the Gestapo discovered his participation in preparations for the July 20th coup attempt. The poem "By Powers of Good" is part of his last surviving letter to his fiancée Maria von Wedemeyer, which he wrote in the Gestapo "house prison" on December 19, 1944. The verses were intended as a "Christmas greeting" for her and his parents and siblings. A few weeks later, on February 7, 1945, Bonhoeffer was taken to Buchenwald concentration camp and finally to Flossenbürg concentration camp, where he was murdered on April 9, 1945 together with Wilhelm Canaris, Hans Oster, and other members of the military resistance.

The poem has frequently been set to music, and is included in a number of hymnals in Germany and abroad. Scarcely another example of religious poetry since the Second World War has become as well known and influential.

Trans. Nancy Lukens, in Letters and Papers from Prison, Dietrich Bonhoeffer Works, vol. 8 © 2010 Fortress Press. Reproduced by special permission of Augsburg Fortress Publishers.

2 Jahre, den wir auseinander leben, liebste Maria. Werde nicht mutlos! Sei du froh, dass Du bei den Eltern bist. Grüsse Deine Mutter u. Großeltern sehr von mir! Hier noch ein paar Verse, die mir in den letzten Abenden einfielen. Sie sind das Weihnachtsgruß für Dich u. die Eltern u. Geschwister.

1. Von guten Mächten treu u. still umgeben
behütet u. getröstet wunderbar, –
so will ich diese Tage mit euch leben
u. mit euch gehen in ein neues Jahr;

2. Noch will das alte unsre Herzen quälen,
noch drückt uns böser Tage schwere Last,
Ach Herr, gib unsern aufgeschreckten Seelen
das Heil, für das Du uns geschaffen hast.

3. Und reichst Du uns den schweren Kelch, den bittern,
des Leids, gefüllt bis an den höchsten Rand,
so nehmen wir ihn dankbar ohne Zittern
aus Deiner guten u. geliebten Hand.

4. Doch willst Du uns noch einmal Freude schenken
an dieser Welt u. ihrer Sonne Glanz,
dann wolln wir des Vergangenen gedenken,
u. dann gehört Dir unser Leben ganz.

5. Lass warm u. hell die Kerzen heute flammen,
die Du in unsre Dunkelheit gebracht,
führ, wenn es sein kann, wieder uns zusammen!
Wir wissen es, Dein Licht scheint in der Nacht

6. Wenn sich die Stille nun tief um uns breitet,
so lass uns hören jenen vollen Klang
der Welt, die unsichtbar sich um uns weitet,
all Deiner Kinder hohen Lobgesang.

7. Von guten Mächten wunderbar geborgen
erwarten wir getrost, was kommen mag.
Gott ist bei uns am Abend u. am Morgen,
u. ganz gewiss an jedem neuen Tag.

Sei mit Eltern u. Geschwistern in
immer Liebe u. Dankbarkeit ge-
grüsst. So meint Dich

Dein Dietrich!

THE SITE OF MEMORY
"TOPOGRAPHY OF TERROR"

FROM REPRESSED "SITE OF THE PERPETRATORS"
TO TOPOGRAPHY OF TERROR DOCUMENTATION CENTER

It was we – not others – who demolished the stone witnesses to Nazi dictatorship after 1945. In any event we did not protest, oddly enough. They were in the way because we wished to erase them from memory, because we could no longer bear to see them. Today we regret the almost complete disappearance of the victims' cells, the torture rooms, and the perpetrators' offices. The architectural evidence is gone, and the living witnesses grow fewer every day.

Dr. Franz Freiherr von Hammerstein, survivor of Buchenwald and Dachau concentration camps, director until 1986 of the Evangelische Akademie Berlin, founding member of the "Initiative für den Umgang mit dem Gestapo-Gelände" formed in 1985, from the foreword to In der Gestapo-Zentrale Prinz-Albrecht-Straße 8. Berichte ehemaliger Häftlinge, Berlin 1989, p. 4.

The Historic Site

Between 1933 and 1945, the headquarters of the Nazi SS and
police state were concentrated in a small area: the Secret State
Police Office, the Reich SS Leadership and from 1939 on the
Reich Security Main Office took possession of the prestigious
buildings on Prinz-Albrecht-Straße and Wilhelmstraße, but
increasingly also used neighboring apartment and commercial
buildings. It was from this site that the persecution of political
opponents of the Nazi regime and persons stamped as "racial
enemies" in Germany and occupied Europe was centrally
controlled. It was here that the genocide of Europe's Jews and
of the Sinti and Roma and the systematic persecution and
murder of other groups were planned and organized. This was
where the special mobile units (Einsatzgruppen) of the Security
Police and Security Service were set up, which sent reports on
the mass murders they committed in Poland and the Soviet
Union back to Berlin. It was also at Prinz-Albrecht-Straße 8 that
the Gestapo set up a "house prison" for those detainees who
were to be interrogated, frequently under torture, at their central
headquarters.

The Origins of the "Topography of Terror"

After the Second World War, the history of this place was
gradually forgotten. By the mid-1950s, virtually all remnants of
the buildings, which had been destroyed or severely damaged in
the war, had been blown up and razed. The former headquarters
of the Gestapo had also been demolished. It had partially burnt
out during the war but, like the Prinz Albrecht Palais, had been
judged capable of reconstruction because of the structural
soundness of the remains. In the early 1960s, when the clearing
of rubble on the properties seemed complete, the traces of this
history appeared to have been erased once and for all, and the
site of the former headquarters of Nazi terror had become a
leveled open space. The circumstance that the site, once
directly adjacent to Berlin's government quarter, had lost its
central location as a result of the war also fostered the process
of forgetting. It was now right on the border between the Soviet
and American sectors. The political division of the city pushed
it to the periphery of West Berlin, where from 1961 it was also
bounded on the north by the Berlin Wall. Finally, the fact that
Prinz-Albrecht-Straße had already disappeared from city maps in
1951, when the East Berlin district of Mitte renamed the street in
honor of the Communist resistance fighter Käthe Niederkirchner,
also helped to bury the site's history. No long-term use for the
terrain emerged, although various land-use plans existed in the
postwar period, including a new philharmonic hall, a helicopter
landing pad or an extension of Kochstraße in Kreuzberg across
the site. Instead, a construction recycling firm moved to the

The street façade of the former
Gestapo headquarters, 1953.

Aerial view of Berlin's former government quarter
along Wilhelmstraße. Below is the cleared site
of the former Reich Security Main Office, 1964.

A construction recycling firm and an "Autodrom" use the former "Gestapo site," June 1981.

Opening event on the former "Gestapo site" for the exhibition "Preußen – Versuch einer Bilanz" presented at the Martin-Gropius-Bau, August 15, 1981.

terrain in the 1970s, and on the southern end the "Autodrom," where people could drive old cars on haphazardly paved roads without a driver's license.

The historic site was only "rediscovered" in the late 1970s. The first indications of the terrain's past emerged during research for the International Building Exhibition (IBA). Associations of former persecutees and civil rights organizations like the International League for Human Rights now pointed to the site's historical significance. The restoration of the neighboring former Museum of Industrial Arts and Crafts to create the Martin-Gropius-Bau exhibition space, and the major exhibition on Prussian history that inaugurated it, "Preußen – Versuch einer Bilanz" (Prussia – Attempt at a Balance), also attracted attention to the site beginning in 1981. After Berlin's parliament debated the site's future for the first time in 1982, the Berlin Senate opened a nationwide competition with international invitations of tenders "to design the site of the former Prinz Albrecht Palais." Of the 194 designs submitted, the jury awarded first prize to the design by the Berlin landscape architects Jürgen Wenzel and Nikolaus Lang. Second prize went to the Italian architect Giorgio Grassi (Milan). In 1984, however, the Senate decided not to realize the project. The complex conceptual formulation of the competition had proved problematic, and the controversies unleashed by the prize-winning design revolved mainly around the questions of whether an artistic treatment of the site was really the right way to go. In the period that followed, various citizens' initiatives, some of them founded expressly for the purpose, but also institutions such as the Akademie der Künste, increasingly campaigned for the site and called for a monument to the victims of National Socialism or a documentation center on the site. In addition, the Verein Aktives Museum (Active Museum Association) and Berlin History Workshop emphasized by means of a symbolic excavation on the terrain in 1985 that the traces of history were by no means lost forever.

In 1987, a temporary exhibition and a design concept for the entire site were realized as part of Berlin's 750th anniversary celebrations. As part of the central historical exhibition "Berlin, Berlin" at the Martin-Gropius-Bau, the documentation "Topography of Terror: Gestapo, SS and Reichssicherheitshauptamt on the 'Prinz-Albrecht-Terrain'," prepared under the direction of the historian Reinhard Rürup, opened in a new exhibition hall by the architect Jürg Steiner (Berlin), which was erected over the remains of the cellars of a former SS mess hut ("kitchen cellar") that had been discovered by chance during construction work. At the same time, research had been done on the terrain with its excavated remains of numerous buildings and traces of the postwar period. Now open to the public, the terrain was equipped with information panels commenting on the site. The remains of the foundations of five cells from the former Gestapo "house prison" were also laid bare. Provided with a temporary roof, they were designated a historic monument one year later. They have been protected since then by a layer of sand. Originally intended for presentation only during the jubilee year, because of its great success the "Temporary Topography of Terror" was extended for an additional year at the end of 1987 and finally for an indefinite period. As then Berlin Senator for Cultural Affairs Volker Hassemer put it, it was to remain "until we can replace it with something better." Lively discussions of what to do with the "Gestapo site" continued into the period of the fall of the Wall and beyond – now also in the context of the new politics of memory in the German capital.

The "Topography of Terror" exhibition hall and site, 1987.

The Topography of Terror Foundation

In February 1989 the Berlin Senate appointed a commission of experts under the chairmanship of Professor Reinhard Rürup, scholarly director of the "Topography of Terror," to develop a concept for the long-range design and use of the site known since the opening of the exhibition as the "Prinz-Albrecht-Terrain." In its final report of March 1990, which also took account of the new situation after the fall of the Wall in November 1989, the commission emphasized the national and international significance of the historic site and recommended the establishment of a documentation and visitor center. The historic site should largely remain as it was with the exposed building remains and traces of the postwar period, with the addition of a permanent site of learning. These recommendations were accepted as the basis for future political decisions by the Berlin House of Representatives and Senate, and shortly thereafter by the German federal government as well. They were also discussed during several days of hearings with the Berlin public, international experts, and organizations of those affected by Nazi terror.

Excavated remains of the foundations of cells from the former "house prison" at Gestapo headquarters, August 1987.

In 1992, the "Topography of Terror," a citizen supported project of the Berliner Festspiele, became an initially dependent foundation under public law. That same year the state of Berlin invited twelve participants to submit designs to an architectural competition for the new documentation center. In 1993, the winner of the first prize, the Swiss architect Peter Zumthor (Haldenstein), was commissioned to realize his design. Eleven years after the competition, however, in May 2004, the state of Berlin and the German federal government as joint sponsors of the Topography of Terror Foundation decided not to complete the building project, which had begun in 1997 and had been halted in 1999 because of technical problems during construction and the risk of exploding costs, which continued to be incalculable. They settled on a new

The permanent exhibition "Topography of Terror" in the excavations along Niederkirchnerstraße, October 2006.

architectural competition. A few weeks before that, Professor Reinhard Rürup had resigned as scholarly director of the Foundation in protest at the continuing construction crisis.

According to the statutes of the "Topography of Terror," which has been an independent foundation since 1995, its purpose is to relay historical information about the Nazi regime and its crimes and to encourage people to actively confront this history, including its aftermath since 1945. In addition, the Foundation is to assume advisory functions for the state of Berlin when relevant issues arise.

Since its founding, the Foundation has been active in a variety of areas. These now include welcoming more than 500,000 visitors a year to the permanent exhibition "Topography of Terror," which has been shown outdoors since 1997 in the excavations along Niederkirchnerstraße, presenting numerous large special exhibitions on the history of the Nazi era in Germany and abroad, developing collections and a specialist library open to the public, organizing national and international conferences, study tours, and seminars as well as public lectures and discussions with scholars from Germany and abroad, coordinating the activities of the German memorial sites with increasingly international networks, and extensive advisory activities within Berlin and German politics. The Foundation has also set up several memorial sites in Berlin in the form of poster documentations and since 2005 has also been responsible for the Documentation Center on Nazi forced labor in Berlin-Schöneweide. As an institution in the German capital, whose profile is defined by the confrontation with the totality of Nazi crimes, the Topography of Terror Foundation thus performs many broader tasks beyond its work on the historic site.

The Use Concept for the Topography of Terror Documentation Center – New Building and Historic Site

The third architectural competition for the site of the "Topography of Terror" was preceded by a period of intense preparation. A public symposium and two specialist colloquia on "Historic Site and Historical Documentation: Building for the Topography of Terror" in the summer/autumn of 2004 offered an opportunity to take stock, reflect anew on the objectives of the "Topography of Terror" project, and, finally, develop the concrete program for the architectural competition under the guidance of the Foundation's managing director Professor Andreas Nachama. The recommendations of the expert commission of 1990 remained the basis for the updated concept, which featured the following central points:

A site not just of German but of European history
"The point of departure for all of the Commission's reflections remains the acknowledgment that the government quarter of the 'SS state'– with the headquarters of the SS, the Gestapo, and the Reich Security Main Office – was a site unique in the history of the Nazi regime and its crimes. Since the politics of repression, persecution, and extermination, which was centered here, extended to all of the European countries under Nazi rule, it is a site not just of German but of European history, and in some respects even of world history. This means that the decisions made about the site and its future function must also meet international standards and expectations."

"Site of the Perpetrators" –
Site of Reflection or Site of Learning
"Although a 'site of the perpetrators' must not ignore the memory of the victims, the focus must clearly be on confronting the political and social conditions under which the crimes became possible and the people who conceived of, organized, and carried them out." The approach to this site thus cannot use the existing memorial sites in former concentration and extermination camps for orientation, it must rather be understood as a 'site of reflection' or a 'site of learning'."
"It must be a place that inspires us to reflect on dictatorship, racism, and inhumanity, that does not diminish the unfathomable nature of Nazi crimes including genocide, but makes education about them possible. There are no models for this, not even internationally. For that reason we will need to blaze new paths in order to do justice to this challenge."

An "open wound" in the city and in German history
The expert commission places a good deal of faith in the expressiveness of the historic site itself. In its present state – its "desolation" and the remains of buildings revealed by excavations – the terrain offers an unusual opportunity "to introduce people to a confrontation with the history of the Nazi system." "The terrain is perceived as a 'disruption' to the familiar – an 'open wound' in the city and in German history as well." With its traces of wartime and postwar history, the impact of the terrain as a whole is jarring. For that reason, the commission expressly opposes any kind of artistic treatment of the terrain. "Anything intrusive that would alter the overall impression is to be avoided. Very restrictive conditions must be placed on any plans for buildings, in particular."

The Foundation's new use concept took up these demands in particular and further accentuated them – all the more after an archaeological dig that began in 1996 in preparation for construction brought to light additional material traces, including remains of the prison yard wall of the former Gestapo "house prison." The call for submissions to the competition ultimately adopted the following of the Foundation's positions on the terrain and the new building:

The site as the "primary object"
"The terrain is a significant component of and the 'primary object' in the 'Topography of Terror' documentation. As a historic site in the center of Berlin, it should be opened to the public in its entirety, and rendered accessible and commented upon historically with an information system (circular tour of the site with 15 stations). Securing the material traces is also of elementary importance. We can dispense with an overall artistic design. The sober character of the terrain should be retained, oriented towards the design of 1987."

"Giving a voice" to the historic site and its traces
"The new building should be attractive to a broad public as a center of documentation and information, of research, teaching and learning and should help to 'give a voice' to the historic site and its traces. The exhibition program, the specialist library, the archive/collections with a series of special databases as well as public events, seminars, and educational programs will offer visitors – from the interested general public and groups of young people to a specialist public with scholarly interests – a wide range of opportunities for information and discussion and in-depth insights into the causes and structures of Nazi dictatorship and its consequences for past and present."

German federal government design
competition for the "Topography of Terror"
site and new documentation center,
April 2005.

Photo: Hans D. Beyer © Stiftung Topographie des Terrors

Computer station for audience statements at the
symposium "Building for the Topography of Terror"
at the Martin-Gropius-Bau on July 9, 2004.

A variety of relationships between inside and outside
"The new building should be perceived as part of the terrain:
it should not cut itself off from its surroundings, but rather
create a lively give and take between the terrain, excavations,
and factual information and invite visitors to take advantage of
what the 'Topography of Terror' has to offer. Especially in the
exhibition and library areas, the building should be transparent
and allow for diverse relationships between inside and outside,
visual links, and correspondences. We should avoid grand urban
planning gestures, obvious symbolism, and any pretentious
museum character. The building's structures should neither
reshape nor dominate the site."

Competition for the Realization
of the "Topography of Terror"

In April 2005 the German federal government invited submissions for the design competition for the "Topography of
Terror" with the express aim of developing an overall concept
for the terrain and a new documentation center that would
do justice to the historic site's national and international
significance in the heart of the capital, while at the same time
not glorifying this "site of the perpetrators." The competition
objective thus encompassed both a concept for the design of
the terrain with all of its material traces and also a design for
a neutral exhibition building with accompanying scholarly and
educational functions. In view of the two previous failed
competitions, having teams of architects and landscape
architects was made an absolute precondition and a budget
set out in advance. The design hierarchy was defined such
that the building should be "subordinated as a service element
to the terrain as the main exhibit." The competition invitation
reiterated the particularity of the "Topography of Terror" as
a project of memory on the "site of the perpetrators:"

"As the third of the great projects of memory in central Berlin,
the 'Topography of Terror', unlike the nearby Berlin Jewish
Museum or the Memorial to the Murdered Jews of Europe, is a
'historic site' that is regarded primarily as a place of scholarly
and educational work and information, not a memorial site."

In all, 309 teams participated in the competition, which was
conducted anonymously in two stages as an open international
bid. In January 2006 the jury unanimously chose the entry by
architect Ursula Wilms (Heinle, Wischer und Partner, Berlin) and
the landscape architect Professor Heinz W. Hallmann (Aachen)
from among the 23 submissions in the second phase of the
competition.

The jury found that the design qualified as a "very interesting and appropriate proposal for the solution of a difficult problem," and noted:

"The documentation center stands as a clear cube in close proximity to the Martin-Gropius-Bau. It makes reference to the latter's ground plan, but is far more reticent in height and external appearance. Nevertheless, it has a certain autonomy and expansiveness. ...

The circumstance that the detachment of the building from the ground produces an impression of lightness and that the design intervenes little in the surrounding landscape is fundamentally positive.

The concept for the outdoor space interprets the situation properly, the exhibition trench, the cells, and the relics of the 'kitchen cellar' are suitably emphasized and integrated into the network of paths."

The New Topography of Terror Documentation Center

Construction on the new Topography of Terror documentation center began officially on November 2, 2007 in the context of a press conference with high-ranking representatives of the Federal Government Commissioner for Culture and the Media and the Federal Ministry of Transport, Building, and Urban Affairs as well as the Governing Mayor of Berlin. The topping-out ceremony was held on May 11, 2009 with numerous representatives and guests from the worlds of politics and society, accompanied by the declaration from the Federal Government Commissioner for Culture and the Media, Minister of State Bernd Neumann:

"With the topping-out ceremony for the 'Topography of Terror' exhibition building after so many years of planning and construction, a crucial step has finally been completed in a project of great importance for the German landscape of memory."

On the whole, the overall concept for the new building and the design of the historic site by the architects Ursula Wilms and Heinz W. Hallmann, various aspects of which have been modified and further developed since the invitation to the competition, delivers on the ideas and aims expressed in the competition.

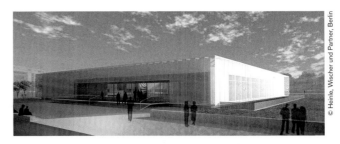

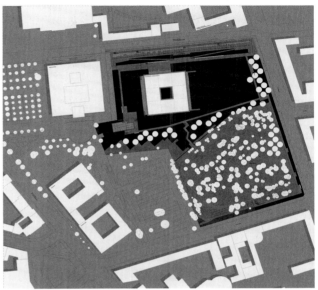

Winning design for the new Topography of Terror Documentation Center by the architect Ursula Wilms and the landscape architect Prof. Heinz W. Hallmann, as of April 2009.

The historic site as the "primary object"
A central characteristic of the site's design is the visual inter-relationship between various material traces on the terrain. With its newly created ground layer of broken gray natural stone, the terrain's open space leaves free only the exposed remains of buildings, the exhibition hall, which is slightly raised off the ground, and the system of walkways, and continues in the grove of locust trees in a linear path along former construction on Wilhelm and Anhalter Straße. The design also integrates the previously inaccessible, partially preserved sidewalk of the former Prinz-Albrecht-Straße on the Berlin Wall. It allows visitors to gain an impression of the original urban layout from the street side, including the remains of the main portal to the former Gestapo headquarters and the driveways. The new glass roof of the widened exhibition trench along the excavations on Niederkirchnerstraße will provide greater transparency and better accessibility for this central area of the "Topography of Terror," in particular. The design of the "house prison" memorial with the remnants of the foundations of the former prison at Gestapo headquarters, which are still protected by a layer of sand and marked by gravel with an inscription set in a metal frame, is restrained. Within the ensemble of historical traces surrounding the memorial, this commemorative site thus contrasts with the still visible remains of the prison yard wall and the exposed cellar rooms of the former SS mess hut, which was originally located outside the plot boundary of Gestapo headquarters on the side of the Prinz Albrecht gardens.

Diverse relationships between inside and outside
The "Topography of Terror" site is visible from all directions from inside the building with its delicate metallic façade. Especially characteristic is the view from the foyer, with its large-scale glass elements, to the north, where one can see the exposed remains of the cellar walls of the former Gestapo headquarters, the Berlin Wall Monument – tangible symbol of the lasting impact of Nazi history – and the imposing dimensions of the monumental former Reich Aviation Ministry on the opposite side of the street. From the building's exhibition space one looks east across an "abrasion" and the barren surface of the terrain to a new

plantation of trees along the building traces on Wilhelmstraße. To the south a vista opens onto the grove of locust trees – a green space contrasting with the sparseness of the rest of the terrain – not least as witness to its treatment in the postwar period. Only the basement-level library looks inward, its rooms grouped around an atrium with a reflecting pool.

"Giving a voice" to the historic site and its traces –
A historical and political place of learning
After years of makeshift arrangements, the new exhibition and documentation center offers the Foundation room for its diverse remits on the site and in its own building. The central areas for visitors to the new building include various exhibition spaces, rooms for a broad range of events and educational programs, and a reference library open to the public, which currently contains some 27,000 volumes on the history of the Nazi era. The building also houses the Topography of Terror Foundation's archives and collections and Institute offices.

Even more than it has thus far, the Foundation will be emphasizing the presentation of exhibitions with its work in the new documentation center. The newly created areas for the permanent exhibitions are closely interrelated, while an additional space in the building for changing and special exhibitions will permit us to go into more depth and supplement themes of the permanent exhibition. The Foundation's executive director Professor Andreas Nachama explains the concept as follows:

"The concept for the three permanent exhibition areas in the new documentation center is based on the idea of portraying the terror exercised by the Gestapo beginning in 1933 and the Reich Security Main Office beginning in 1939 from various narrative perspectives, which – much like an adjustable magnifying glass – brings the visitor ever closer to the crimes conceived and coordinated from this place. The circular walking tour along the material traces on the 'Topography of Terror' terrain allows visitors to experience the site's history in the stricter sense of the word. The exhibition trench focuses on Berlin in the Third Reich, rendering visible the addresses of Nazi terror in the city. The permanent exhibition 'Topography of Terror' in the new hall illustrates the anatomy of the SS state with examples, including the biographies of Nazi perpetrators, and a documentation of Nazi crimes in Germany and Nazi-occupied Europe. Using chosen examples, the exhibition also documents how this history has been studied and dealt with from 1945 to the present."

The new exhibition and documentation building as well as the newly designed historic site opened for May 8, 2010, the 65th anniversary of the end of the Second World War. In the former and, since 1990, new German capital, the Topography of Terror Documentation Center allows for a critical confrontation with Nazi crimes and their political and social preconditions on the "site of the perpetrators." Understood as a site of memory and warning, the documentation center incorporates at the same time the commemoration of the victims of the Nazi system. With expanded offerings in exhibitions and events, and as a host to other institutions working in the fields of historical and political education, the Topography of Terror Documentation Center is a place of learning and a discussion forum. As such it forms, finally, part of the Berlin capital network and the national and international landscape of memory. Based on its memory work, it aims to promote a better understanding of human and civil rights, the rule of law, democracy, and tolerance in the present with an eye to the future.

Photo: Stefan Müller © Stiftung Topographie des Terrors

View of the permanent exhibition "Topography of Terror" from the foyer, June 2010.

BIBLIOGRAPHY

Rosmarie Beier/Leonore Koschnick, Der Martin-Gropius-Bau. Geschichte und Gegenwart des ehemaligen Kunstgewerbemuseums, 2nd edn, Berlin 1988.

Andreas Bekiers and Karl Robert Schütze, Zwischen Leipziger Platz und Wilhelmstraße. Das ehemalige Kunstgewerbemuseum zu Berlin und die bauliche Entwicklung seiner Umgebung von den Anfängen bis heute, Berlin 1981.

Berlin 1933–1945. Between Propaganda and Terror, ed. Stiftung Topographie des Terrors, Berlin 2010.

Berlin – „Germania". Die projektierte Zerstörung Berlins durch Albert Speers Planungen der Nord-Süd-Achse für „Germania" als Hauptstadt eines großgermanischen Weltreiches, Karte und Begleitheft mit Beiträgen von Felix Escher, Berlin n.d. [2004].

Berlin. Planungsgrundlagen für den städtebaulichen Ideenwettbewerb „Hauptstadt Berlin", ed. Bundesminister für Wohnungsbau and Senator für Bau- und Wohnungswesen, Berlin 1957.

Erika Bucholtz, Die Zentralen des nationalsozialistischen SS- und Polizeistaats. Gebäudenutzung und Bauplanung in Berlin 1933–1945, Zeitschrift für Geschichtswissenschaft 52, no. 12 (2004): 1106–25.

Büttner, Königlicher Baurat, Der Erweiterungsbau des Königlichen Kunstgewerbemuseums in Berlin, Zentralblatt der Bauverwaltung LVIII (1908): cols 509–28.

Laurenz Demps, Berlin-Wilhelmstraße. Eine Topographie preußisch-deutscher Macht, Berlin 1994.

Laurenz Demps et al, Bundesfinanzministerium. Ein belasteter Ort? – The Federal Ministry of Finance. Can History Taint a Building?, Berlin 2002.

Matthias Donath, Architektur in Berlin 1933–1945. Ein Stadtführer, ed. Landesdenkmalamt Berlin, Berlin 2004.

Jost Dülffer et al, Hitlers Städte. Baupolitik im Dritten Reich. Eine Dokumentation, Cologne 1978.

Helmut Engel et al (eds), Geschichtslandschaft Berlin. Orte und Ereignisse, vol. 5: Kreuzberg, Berlin 1994.

Geschichtsmeile Wilhelmstraße – Historic Wilhelmstraße, ed. Stiftung Topographie des Terrors, Berlin 2006.

The "House Prison" at Gestapo Headquarters in Berlin. Terror and Resistance 1933–1945, ed. Stiftung Topographie des Terrors, 2nd rev. and enlarged edn, Berlin 2007.

Albert Heilmann, Das Europa-Haus in Berlin. Ein neuzeitlicher Großbau. Seine Entstehungsgeschichte vom ersten Spatenstich bis zur Vollendung, Berlin 1931.

Jürgen Henkys, Geheimnis der Freiheit. Die Gedichte Dietrich Bonhoeffers aus der Haft. Biographie | Poesie | Theologie, Gütersloh 2005.

Hans-Hermann Hertle, Die Berliner Mauer. Monument des Kalten Krieges – The Berlin Wall. Monument of the Cold War, Bonn 2007.

Friedrich Hetzelt, Das Palais Prinz Albrecht in Berlin. Dem Andenken des SS-Obergruppenführers Reinhard Heydrich, Zentralblatt der Bauverwaltung 63, no.1/2 (1943), (Berlin, January 13, 1943): 1–15.

In der Gestapo-Zentrale Prinz-Albrecht-Straße 8. Berichte ehemaliger Häftlinge. Eine Dokumentation der Evangelischen Akademie Berlin (West), Berlin 1989.

Ludwig Münz, Führer durch die Behörden und Organisationen, 4th edn, Berlin 1939.

Mythos Germania. Schatten und Spuren der Reichshauptstadt. Eine Ausstellung des Berliner Unterwelten e.V., Berlin 2008.

Joachim Petsch, Baukunst und Stadtplanung im Dritten Reich. Herleitung, Bestandsaufnahme, Entwicklung, Nachfolge, Munich 1976.

Der Preußische Landtag. Bau und Geschichte, ed. Präsidentin des Abgeordnetenhauses von Berlin, Berlin 1993.

Realisierungswettbewerb Topographie des Terrors. Berlin. 309 Entwürfe – Katalog zur Ausstellung der Wettbewerbsarbeiten, ed. Stiftung Topographie des Terrors and Bundesamt für Bauwesen und Raumordnung, Berlin 2006.

Hans J. Reichhardt and Wolfgang Schäche, Von Berlin nach Germania. Über die Zerstörungen der „Reichshauptstadt" durch Albert Speers Neugestaltungsplanungen, completely rev. and expanded edn, Berlin 1998.

Wolfgang Schäche, Architektur und Städtebau in Berlin zwischen 1933 und 1945. Planen und Bauen unter der Ägide der Stadtverwaltung, 2nd edn, Berlin 1992.

Jan Erik Schulte, Zwangsarbeit und Vernichtung: Das Wirtschaftsimperium der SS. Oswald Pohl und das SS-Wirtschafts-Verwaltungshauptamt 1933–1945, Paderborn 2001.

Johannes Sievers, Bauten für die Prinzen August, Friedrich und Albrecht von Preußen. Ein Beitrag zur Geschichte der Wilhelmstraße in Berlin, Berlin 1954.

Topography of Terror. Gestapo, SS and Reichssicherheitshauptamt on the "Prinz-Albrecht-Terrain." A Documentation, ed. Reinhard Rürup, 16th rev. and enlarged edn, Berlin 2006 (1st German edn, Berlin 1987).

Topography of Terror. Gestapo, SS and Reich Security Main Office on Wilhelm- and Prinz-Albrecht-Straße. A Documentation, ed. Stiftung Topographie des Terrors, Berlin 2010.

Johannes Tuchel and Reinold Schattenfroh, Zentrale des Terrors. Prinz-Albrecht-Straße 8: Hauptquartier der Gestapo, Berlin 1987.

Helmut Weihsmann, Bauen unterm Hakenkreuz. Architektur des Untergangs, Vienna 1998.

Hans Wilderotter, Alltag der Macht. Berlin Wilhelmstraße, Berlin 1998.

Die Wilhelmstraße. Regierungsviertel im Wandel – Wilhelmstraße. The Government Quarter through the Centuries, ed. Stiftung Topographie des Terrors, Berlin 2007.

Susanne Willems, Der entsiedelte Jude. Albert Speers Wohnungsmarktpolitik für den Berliner Hauptstadtbau, Berlin 2000.